639·220<del></del>

**IRF**    ·   ⊤⊤   **UNC**

# *The North Ships*

## The Life of a Trawlerman

### STEVEN PIPER

CHESHIRE COUNTY LIBRARY
WITHDRAWN
18 OCT 1974
FOR SALE
639 220924
001400

## DAVID & CHARLES

NEWTON ABBOT   LONDON
NORTH POMFRET (VT)   VANCOUVER

ISBN 0 7153 6483 9
Library of Congress Catalog Card Number 74-76187
© E. M. Spargo 1974

All rights reserved. No part of this publication
may be reproduced, stored in a retrieval system,
or transmitted, in any form or by any means,
electronic, mechanical, photocopying, recording or otherwise, without the prior permission
of David & Charles (Holdings) Limited

Set in 11 on 13 point Garamond and printed in
Great Britain by Latimer Trend & Company
Ltd Plymouth for David & Charles (Holdings)
Limited  South Devon House  Newton Abbot
Devon

Published in the United States of America
by  David  &  Charles  Inc  North  Pomfret
Vermont 05053 USA

Published in Canada by Douglas David &
Charles  Limited    3645  McKechnie  Drive
West Vancouver BC

# Contents

# List of Illustrations

CHAPTER I

# *Arrival*

I remember that I arrived in Hull late one winter's evening and found lodgings in a house near the station. I had no more than a pound or two in my pocket and it was difficult to persuade the landlady to take me in.

'I like lodgers to pay in advance,' she said, and remained unmoved when I pointed to my bag. All that could be said for it was that it was made of thick canvas and had a handle decorated by a few fancy knots. As security it did look thin and light. She knew as well as I did that there wasn't much in it if it should come to claiming baggage for unpaid bills.

'I've come more than thirteen thousand miles to get here. Let me in tonight and I'll give you a good backhander tomorrow.'

'I'll have to see the Captain,' she said. She shut the door but I noticed she left it on the latch. In a minute she was back and stood aside in the doorway to let me in.

'He says you can have the back room at the top.' I would have taken a bed on the attic landing, I was so glad to be inside the house. She bustled up the stairs in front of me and at the top of the house—where it could be seen that not much money had been spent on comfort—she swung open a door made of groove and tongue deal. It had a latch, I remember, like the ones supplied for shed doors. You pressed a lever with the thumb, a bar rattled up, released the door and rattled down when you took your thumb off. The room was, in fact, very like a small shed built inside a house and looked almost as cold as the pavement I had just left. But the bed seemed good and there was certainly nothing to be gained from a stand for better conditions. I was glad to be there.

'You can come down for supper when you're ready,' she said. Something unexpected. An extra. She went off down the stairs and I unpacked my few things.

9

I knocked on the door at the back of the ground floor and heard her tell me to come in. It was a kitchen, down two steps, a room much longer than it was wide, and the ceiling was low. The architect must have run out of space when the time came in his plan to put in a good-sized kitchen. Apart from the landlady there were two other beings at home in there, a big old man in loose clothes, a heavy suit draped around his bony shoulders, and a parrot.

'This is the Captain,' she said. He didn't look like a ship's master to me, too broken down for that.

'We're just going to have something to eat,' he said. Later on I found out that he was no ship's captain but a retired foreman of stevedores. He had been a captain in the army in 1920, supervising the loading and discharging of ships in Liverpool. But only his wife called him Captain now. The few people he talked to always called him Mr Adams or Harold, but she kept up the military rank.

The supper was on the table. There was a plate of three cold pickled pigs' feet, white and dry looking. Incisions had been made in the joints so they would be easy to eat, and the meat had pulled away from the cuts leaving the knuckle ends protruding. I had never seen anything less appetising.

'Sit opposite the Captain,' she said. We sat down and she served a pig's foot to each of us. There was nothing to eat with it except slices of white bread which had been scraped over with melted butter; there was also a bottle of tomato sauce on the table.

'Nothing I like more,' said the landlady, and as daintily as possible she began to gnaw the meat from the very small bones. The Captain grunted his approval and the parrot sidled up and down on the perch placed on the floor between them. A united family.

I didn't think my position in the house was secure enough to refuse the food or to leave it uneaten once I had accepted it. I began to eat; I can remember the meal to this day. The meat tasted strongly of the fluid in which it had been preserved and no matter how much each mouthful was chewed it was amazingly difficult to swallow. I managed to get rid of it by easing each mouthful down my throat with a draught of tea. By the time I had finished my share it was touch and go whether I vomited. I could feel my forehead was damp and the sweat was prickling at the roots of my hair.

When the meal was over and cleared away she brought us more tea, and we sat around the big stove let into the wall at the scullery end of the kitchen. She was out for a talk.

'He's come thirteen thousand miles,' she said to the Captain. 'What've you come all that way for?'

'I've come to join a trawler.'

'Join a trawler? I don't want anyone from this house going away in those ships. You go back where you've come from. Those men do this town no good. Decent people won't have anything to do with them.'

'But don't they put more fish ashore in Hull than any other port in the world? Haven't fishermen made Hull what it is? It's a famous port, isn't it?'

She admitted nothing. Silenced by her own mute dislike of all fishermen and their ships, the Captain and I drank our tea. I took the chance to think of what I'd heard of these ships and their crews.

I had been seafaring for ten years and my experience of ships was as wide as most seamen's. Whenever the subject of hard ships had come up or the talk was of heavy cash rewards for dangerous voyages it was always about trawlermen I had heard, and especially about the deep-water men of Hull. In Australia I spent eighteen months in the little longshore trawlers which work out of Sydney up and down the coast to Tasmania. It was a new sort of seafaring for me and I was impressed by what I thought were the expert crews, by the problems set by the gear they handled, and by the long hours they worked.

I served a rough apprenticeship as a trawlerman in those little old-fashioned 200-ton ships and was proud of myself when they rated me Third Hand. Then I shipped for a voyage with an old emigrated Yorky signed on the same ship, a Hull man, who did not bother to hide what he thought of us.

'You don't know the game,' he would say. 'There isn't one of you'd make a good snacker on a Hull ship,' meaning a deck boy. He was too old to be much more than a passenger when it came to heavy work, but we all recognised him for what he was when a quick repair to the gear was necessary. His technique with the wooden netting needle was a picture of dexterity, delicacy and strength. By watching him I learned the way to lay out the torn net and how to bend the four kinds of hitch which are used in the trawl. He showed me how to use my knife on a tear so that the mesh of the net could be replaced exactly. He told me about the giant trawls which are used in the White Sea, off Greenland and Iceland, and on the banks of Bear Island.

One day, off the south-east coast of Australia, under the lee of Wilson's Promontory and nicely off the land, we were dodging into a gale. The gear was aboard and everything was battened down; Yorky and I were on watch on the bridge. Our job was to keep the weather comfortably on the bow. We had the engines balanced against the rudder and the weather coming over the Cape, and all it needed was a spoke or two of the wheel from side to side. Though the movement of the ship was always there, we two were wedged into the structure of the bridge and counted it an enjoyable evening. It was a great rest from fishing and Yorky began to tell me about Hull.

I signed off that little ship when we docked in Sydney and went to say goodbye.

'Going to float out of Hull, are you?' was all he said. 'Well, you might be all right.'

That was thirteen thousand miles away, and now I was listening to other views on trawlermen and fishing from a different sort of Hull citizen.

'The trouble with those men is they get too much money.'

'Good night, Missus. Good night, Captain,' I said, and went up to bed.

I didn't want breakfast at that lodging house so I got up before the Captain and his wife were about and went out to look at the town.

# *Hull*

Every trade has its centre, where a man goes when he wants to know the best way to do things. It must have been a fine thing to have shipped aboard a Bristol ship in the days when things were, or were not, 'Bristol fashion'. No doubt men in Bristol ships were treated worse than most, for the phrase must have stood for a terrible lot of sweat and toil; yet a man who had paid off a Bristol ship, a man who had a voyage or two behind him in such ships, even a man who perhaps was prepared to swear never to float from Bristol again, such a one could settle back on a shade more self-esteem than others. Thus when engines were driven by steam it was engineers trained on the Clyde who were the undisputed masters of them. You could find out how to build a ship on the Tyneside if you were a hard enough man to learn there, and today those young fellows who decide very early that they must know how to make money can be found in the City of London. But if you want to learn about cod and haddock you have to go to Hull, where the course in practical ichthyology includes subsidiary instruction in plaice, halibut and skate.

Not that everyone in Hull draws his living from the trawlers. Hull is a big city with a wide range of work. It is the second biggest sea-port in the land; they make metal boxes there; there is a big manufacturer of medical supplies; someone erected a paint factory which employs a thousand or two. Then there are all the men and women who carry on the business of business. Things are bought and sold by the ton, deals are made and people are as much at the mercy of each other in Hull as they are anywhere else. But none of this gives it its stature. The thing in which it has its special character, the special flavour, the smell of its commerce comes from the Fish Dock. The five or six thousand men who man the trawlers, the same sort of number whose lives are more or less bound up ashore with them, from the men who build and maintain them, through the 'bobbers' who unload them, the filleters who carve up the catch, through extra numbers of dependants, wives, widows, mothers, fathers, children, trawler owners, through the publicans whose trade comes from pleasure-bent fishers, right down to the landlord who owns a row of Fish Dock cottages, all these provide the blood stream which gives the city its vitality. Like all human blood it contains its proportion of bad.

When I had arrived the night before it was dark and there was not much more than a glimmer of daylight now in this winter's dawn. In the main part of the city the people were hurrying to work. I knew the habits of shipping offices and the hours they kept and I myself was in no hurry. For an unemployed hand there would be nothing going on until the middle of the forenoon. I was hungry and began to look for a café.

Now Hull is no Venice. There are no canals for popular thoroughfares, no open-air café life, cathedrals or piazzas, and there are no ships settling their account with the shore among people's lives at the end of the street. Nor is it like London, where dock life goes on unseen behind tall brick walls, where you can see nothing of berthed ships, or of ships being warped ahead or astern a few fathoms to match a hold to a crane, or cargo work going on. And Hull is no Southampton, where the ships make fast to quays built miles beyond the city, constructed on windy reclaimed marshlands. In Hull, right in the middle of the city, I saw a dock separated from the main square by nothing more than a 6 feet high iron railing. One end of the railing was let into the structure surrounding a solid looking art gallery and the other finished up in an agglomeration of shops, a news stand, and the beginning of a street. I had never seen anything like it in any other city port, the shore end of the sea reaching right into its heart. Floating high out of the water, a stone's throw from the railing where I stood, was a small ship.

She was unfinished and by the look of her trim there was still a good deal of her heavy gear to be put aboard. I was looking at her from a point broad on her bow and could see the wide flare coming away from the stem and the very soft forward lines of that part of the hull which would soon be below the water line. She looked resilient and buoyant.

There are times when a ship, stemming heavy weather, will lift her forefoot so far out of the sea that from another deck can be seen a fearful length of her keel, as far back as a vertical taken through her forward hatches. This ship looked as though, in the worst of weather, she could re-enter the water without that terrible crash that makes the seaman think hard of the skill of the shipyard where his ship was built. She was very high in the bow with a steep sheer down to her waist under the bridge. She was not in any way to be compared with an ordinary ship of commerce big or small, whose design is based on the greatest possible quantity of load. Her designer must have thought first of the shape of his ship, of her speed, of her all-round ability to survive the weather, and only then, it seemed to me, did he come to the question of where she would stow her load. She looked to be the result of great accumulated experience, her shape as right for the job as a ladle's is for serving stew. She was the first distant-water trawler I ever saw.

# CHAPTER 3

# *The Hessle Road*

I wandered back to the railway station for my breakfast and sat about at leisure for an hour or so among the travellers. While I was at the counter for a third cup of tea, the swing door which led in from the big arrival and departure hall burst open, and an old tramp in ragged clothes stood there and stared in at all of us. Keeping the door wide with an outstretched arm, he looked us over and shouted 'Ha!' There was a moment's silence. Everyone in the café looked at the doorway, but the tramp had nothing more to say. He went off.

The café noise started again, but there was no doubt that many sitting there had been outraged. One or two tried to laugh away their discomfort, but a shout of scorn such as the ragged old man had let loose among the tables was not to be drowned by a giggle or two, or by pretending that it had not happened, or even by dismissing the intruder as a lunatic. There's a sign, I thought: Elijah. I remembered the incident in *Moby Dick* when Ishmael and Queequeg, newly signed on their whaler, are met by a crazed old sailor who follows them down the quayside, full of portents and forecasts of disaster.

'Tell them I've concluded not to make one of them,' he says to Ishmael, meaning that nothing would persuade him aboard the ship that they had just shipped in.

I had to accept my share of the old man's contempt for all our hopes; I could not get the tone of his jeer out of my mind.

By now it was nearing ten o'clock and I began to make for the Fish Dock.

If you are a seafarer you may have heard of the Hessle Road, but since I have read no books which give a paragraph or two to this famous street I'm not too proud to give the reader a glimpse of the way it looked to me when I was there.

It is a long street that leads out of Hull, skirts the upstream docks and the railway yards, and, inside those yards, generally follows the contour of the river towards the village of Hessle. Walking out of Hull you have on your right the sort of shops you would expect to find on a working-class main road; provision shops, shops which sell cheap clothing to families with neither time nor money enough to use the expensive stores in the town centre, a big draper's shop, enough pawn shops to cover the credit needs of the local community, public houses, and all of these mixed up with ugly domestic accommodation, some of it at street level and some in flats above the shops. That was the right hand side of the Hessle Road itself.

But on that same side and coming into the road were numbers of streets of very heavily built and substantial dwellings. They must have been erected fifty or sixty years ago on a strong base of prosperity by those thrusting clear of a working-class environment, putting a main road, the Hessle Road, between that class and themselves; no doubt some of them were owners of Hessle Road shops who had made money there. I knew a middle-aged spinster, sister of an elderly pharmaceutical chemist for whom she kept house, who owned their villa in one of the streets. Also bookmakers had property there, and while I was in Hull I saw in those streets a few brass plates denoting the habitations of doctors, dentists and solicitors, professional men, well afloat but not to be called rich. These were good streets and the houses were cared for, the bricks were pointed from time to time and I often saw the vans and paraphernalia of firms of decorators.

But, as usual, times had changed and it was clear that the people who lived there had to take great pains to keep up their respectable standard of living, for where docks and ships and railway tracks lie just over the horizon, problems must be faced by those not willing to admit the debts they owe to dockers, seafarers and railwaymen. They have to keep themselves to themselves if they are to stay snug in their class, that is if the value of their property is to be maintained, and this is always a hard thing to do. These Canutes were quite incapable of pushing back the tide. Thus in a big outhouse I knew, attached to a piece of property right in the middle of one of these tidy looking streets a man who had at heart the interests of trawlermen and others out for liquor—he himself was out for money—had established a drinking club.

When the public houses closed at three o'clock, numbers of taxis used to draw up outside the club and with plenty of slamming of doors and outspoken obscenity, the semi-drunken men would pour inside. The roof was made of corrugated iron and provided a fine sounding board for the uproarious music within. Sometimes a man was seen to vomit in the street; and into the taxis, constantly coming and going, would lurch drinkers with the women they had found in the club. They were bound for one or other of the private brothels which had also little by little been established in that good neighbourhood. Any estate agent commissioned to buy would have been bound to point out that change was taking place there; and the agent selling, no matter how he demanded admiration for the quality of the building in his deal, could scarcely have denied it. Property was getting cheap.

That was the right hand side of the Hessle Road as I remember it, not on that first day, but as I got to know it later; still respectable but getting profane in parts.

But on that day it so happened that I walked to the Fish Dock on the left hand side of the Hessle Road. It is a long time since I tried to recall that street but it seems to me now that the side I was on had more poverty about it, more signs of hard times; there were shops where you could buy faggots and cooked peas, steamy little ovens of shops, not in the least like those cafés equipped with the latest apparatus for serving fried fish and chips. But they filled a local social need. A meal of faggots and peas could cost less than a cooked meal at home, if you counted in the price of the gas. I found out later when money was short that they were good places. Also on this side was the Fisherman's Bethel. I never went inside the Bethel and I never knew, throughout the years I spent at Hull, a single trawlerman who tried the hard spiritual tack no doubt administered in there. Further down was the finest building in the road, the cinema, finer even than the Bethel itself, for though that refuge was built of the best materials, stone and brick with a good roof, it still could not match the cinema for the sight of money lavishly spent, neither, by the look of it, was it as warm and comfortable inside on a cold winter's evening.

I could see that the little streets leading into this side of the road were very different from those opposite, for these contained authentic working-class homes. At the Hull end of the Hessle Road some of the terraces had front yards, simply a fenced-off break from the pavement in which on a rare fine day a woman could put out a baby's pram. But passing the Bethel you came to streets leading away from the road down to the railway tracks where the front doors were built right on to the pavement.

Getting near docks, I thought, for the place reminded me of streets in the dockland I had lived in at Sydney—Woolloomoolloo. The weather, true enough, was better there, but there was the same evidence of rich men erecting cheap rows of small dwellings for poor men to live in. But this is what always follows the embedding of money. You can see, anywhere in the world, the local equivalent of this sort of housing for workmen, around any group of factories, docks and railway yards, where they have to earn their living; cheap barrack districts for the night-time storage of labour when it is not actually in use.

The street I wanted had about it a look, when at last I found it, of being the centre of local vitality. The houses were no different from those in the other little streets, but for a start it had three important buildings at its Hessle Road end. Just before the corner was the cinema already mentioned, just inside the street was a building I was to know as the St Andrew's Club, and opposite, on the other corner, was a big and ugly public house named Pine's. This had been given me as my landmark and into West Dock Avenue I turned.

The day was grey, the atmosphere was thick, and even the bricks of the buildings, porous though they were, looked damp. I don't believe that the contractor who put up this street of terraced boxes, known as houses, would have been cynic enough to call it an avenue; he must have been too busy amassing money to have had time to waste on humour, no matter how vicious.

The street was short but aside from the two big buildings and the terraces of houses it also had a handful of shops, mainly selling clothing for fishermen. The shops were small, matching the size of the houses, and the shopkeepers were forced to make as best use they could of their limited space for display and storage. The windows were packed with all the special warm clothing which fishermen need, and to get through the doors and into the shops it was necessary to push aside the foliage of hanging bunches of sea-boots, white, red and clerical grey, and the rubber and plastic frocks, blue-green, bright yellow and black. The road was bisected by two 'rows', that is little lanes, no more than asphalt footpaths, of half a dozen houses of the same type as the ones fronting the avenue.

I walked the two hundred yards down the street to where it swung to the right and the housing came to a stop at the limit of the railway yards. There the road turned into a steep cobbled ramp leading down to a tunnel under a railway bridge, soaking overhead and underfoot in the damp winter atmosphere.

At the end of the tunnel, through which passed a continuous stream of all kinds of traffic—trucks, cars, taxis, horse-carts, men—another ramp led upwards out of this darkness and the echoing din and the wet on to the entrance of the Fish Dock. I came to know that road well during the next years.

CHAPTER 4

# St Andrew's Dock, Known as the Fish Dock

The dock has to deal with about three thousand five hundred tons of fish every week, which are put ashore between Monday and Friday mornings by an average of four to five ships per day. This is the basic fact of the Fish Dock and everything to be seen there is in one way or another bound up with the job of keeping this daily shoal coming ashore.

The dock was built in two parts as a rectangle about 700 yards long and under 100 yards wide, stretching along the north bank of the Humber and bisected about half-way along its length by a ramp and a steel swing-bridge. The half to the west is newly excavated, and that on the east or Hull side of the bridged passage is the old dock.

Now the Humber is a river with a big rise and fall of tide, in fact at low water of the full spring tides the entrance to the Fish Dock very nearly dries. Therefore to keep the dock full of water a lock basin had to be constructed at the river entrance in the corner of the old dock with heavily built gates at each end of it, big enough to float a trawler. To fill this basin takes a very large volume of water which, when the tide is ebbing and has dropped below a certain depth, cannot be spared from what is inside the dock, for enough water must always be kept there to keep the docked ships afloat and to permit them to manoeuvre as they discharge, refuel, take on ice and so on. Thus at the time of day when the ebbing tide has reached its critical depth the lock gates are shut at the order of the dockmaster and will not be reopened until the flood has again risen to the necessary level. During this time ships may neither leave nor enter, and any ship arriving at the Fish Dock even five minutes late on the completion of her voyage must lie off in the river at anchor until the dock-master deems the flood full enough for the lock gates to be opened. Only then, and singly, may they come alongside the outside quay or 'bullnose'. They face downstream to stem the flood for safe ship handling in the proper seamanlike way, and then manoeuvre, stern first with engines and warps, through the lock basin and into the dock. To 'miss a tide', as the saying goes, can add seven hours to the trip, can often mean a similar reduction to the men's valuable time ashore, and, as we will see later, can also be a factor of terrible and dangerous significance in the last days of the voyage.

If we imagine we are looking right over the after end of a trawler which is pointing her stern into the dock, then immediately on our left hand is a long quayside where as many as eight or ten vessels will be lying head to us, empty of fish and now loading stores and fuel for the next voyage. As we come in and the lock gates are opened to the ebb or flood of the tide the level of the water in the dock will suddenly rise or fall an inch, according to the tide's state, and the moored ships will noticeably throw their weight on to their mooring lines. If the dock is quiet we will hear those lines crack and stretch around the ship's bitts and the shore bollards before they take up the strain, for as long as a ship floats she will move to the tide and wind; even in the most peaceful of docks, under the shelter of warehouses, she will always nudge and strain at the slack of her ropes.

At right angles to us is the short boundary of the dock. The offices and store lofts of the two biggest trawling companies are built a few yards back from this edge and there are normally one or two of their vessels tied up there. Over on the right is the other wall and it is this one that vessels returned from a voyage make for. This is the fish market, where the catch is sold, where the filleters do their carving, and where the fish merchants and the trawler owners divide up a fortune between them.

Back on our left (the ship still stern into the dock), fronting the road which runs the whole length of this side of the dock, are the offices and subsidiary buildings of more trawling companies, one of which, when I was there, was Hellyers of ominous reputation among trawlermen. Their food was said to be the worst on the dock, but their ships, it was added, were tuned to the highest pitch of efficiency. Aboard a Hellyers' ship you always worked at top speed, the trawl was 'shot', the catch hauled, the fish gutted and below faster than in the ships of any other company. Tales of the abnormal savagery, of the exceptional and barbaric inhumanity of Hellyers' skippers were commonplace. But I shipped for a few voyages with Hellyers' and I found things no worse there than in any other company.

I believe these fishermen's yarns were encouraged by trawler owners, probably even winked at by the Hellyer brothers themselves, on the principle that a ready-made target for the exasperation of exploited men was a very handy decoy. All sorts of inconspicuous hardships could then be lumped in with the accumulated load already borne by trawlermen if the men persuaded themselves that, at the least, they were better off than 'Hellyers' gadgers'. And as for the brothers themselves, well, there would always be hands to make their numbers up. I remember aboard a ship of theirs how conversation would turn wistfully on the chance of a berth in a ship belonging to another firm.

Past the engineering shops and near the end of the long dockside, constructed on the river embankment, is a vast mincing machine and fish-fry combined called the fishmeal factory, a vital component of the profit of trawler owners and the loss of fishermen. But leaving aside for a chapter or two the part played by this robber in fishermen's lives, let me try to put down a brief description of it for it is a very important piece of Fish Dock gear.

It is a slab-sided factory enmeshed in pipes containing, no doubt, the water and steam necessary for the perpetual cooking of a giant meal. But it was a place which cost me so much unwilling money that neither I, nor many trawlermen I knew, ever had the heart to go in to look at it. Nevertheless, I take it that inside there must have been apparatus for mincing the flesh and bones of the tons of fish poured into the numerous hoppers which were fixed in the factory wall at dock level. There must also have been equipment for drying the cooked preparation, for compacting it, for cutting it into that size of cake or cube which makes it an appetising meal for a cow; and no doubt there was pulverising gear for turning it into a

23

species of bran suitable for spreading about as manure on fields and gardens. But I find it difficult to recall in detail for I never looked at the mill except in rage as the crematorium of thousands of foot-pounds of my unpaid labour.

Finally at the extreme end of the dock, at right angles to the two long walls and joining them, was the slipway where, in cradles mounted on wide railway tracks, trawlers could be hauled out of the water to have the barnacles cleaned off them and examinations and maintenance carried out on the hull.

I knew a man once, not a seaman, who was compelled for a month or more for doubtless good reasons of his own, to ship in a schooner trading about the Mediterranean. It so happened that soon after he signed we drydocked. The skipper, who was also part owner, was a Rumanian and not the man to pay shore labour when he had dock-idle hands in his own fo'c's'le, nor was the country we were in noted then for the strength of its trade union movement. The result was that the dock gang was bought off with a backhander (and knowing that skipper I assume that it was none too generous) and instead of a comfortable forty-eight hours ashore we found ourselves on the dock floor, under the hull with scrapers and wire brushes in our hands, black with muck, and the hair of our heads fouled with the dried barnacles we were scraping down. The new hand and I were working alongside one another. The sun was hot and was looking into our side of the dock. Suddenly he said, 'You know, we're performing the most intimate functions on her bottom.'

'We're doing what?'

'Yes. And her most intimate organs are exposed to anybody's gaze.'

He paid off soon after that, but I never forgot that lunatic chat, and I can never look at ships in drydock or on the slip without that lush comparison coming back to mind. But here in Hull trawlermen did not clean off their own ships. The slipway gangs were properly organised and much of the job was done with machines.

Once I completed a voyage in a ship due for the slip on her return. We went ashore on docking with our usual small gear leaving our bulky waterproof clothing aboard. The next morning after settling our account with the company, we signed off with instructions to get out belongings before she was slipped. But that noon, I remember, I was roystering with some old friends I had come across ashore, and was in no mind to be loaded with two pairs of thigh boots, three rubber frocks, two sou'westers, a mattress and blankets. I left it all aboard and it was slipped with the ship. The next day I had to make my way along the Fish Dock in a taxi to fetch it and left the car at the fish-meal factory while I walked over the steel tracks of the slipway to where she lay.

Heavy gear is needed to slip a ship of five or six hundred tons displacement. I was able to have a good look at the construction of the cradles. They are made of pairs of massive soft timbers bedded on heavy steel frames in which bearings are mounted for the flanged wheels. (Soft wood is used to avoid damaging the hull.) The cradle is let down the ramp of the slip deep into the water and the ship is then winched head on to the slip between guiding posts until she grounds gently on the cradle timbers with her keel lined up to fit between them. Ship and cradle are then winched up the ramp until the whole of her hull is supported, wedges being knocked in where necessary to give maximum hold. The big six-fold wire 'purchases', with one end led to the drum of a great winch, then take up the total strain and cradle and ship are hove slowly up the slip. It is a nice thing to watch, and if the art of seamanship is the moving of heavy weights under the worst conditions then slipway work is one delicate part of it. There's many an old sailor in a slipway gang (and incidentally there's many another in the crew who rig the big top in a travelling circus).

When the ship is high and dry, the whole beautiful line of her hull visible out of the water, she is jacked off the cradle and supported on timbers under the keel and by heavy posts, securely fixed with wedges, under the curve of her bilges. The work required to be done on her is then carried out. When the time comes to put her back to sea the whole process is reversed. She is hove slowly down the slip with the purchase rove the other way, and at the point where the water begins to take her weight she floats off the cradle and with a gentle run glides stern first into the dock, nicely controlled by ropes (known as springs), leading away from her bitts aft and forward to strong points on the shore.

There was a ladder rigged at her side and I climbed up and over the gunwale on to her foredeck. Now I am not one of those who lash themselves into fantasies of admiration and dislike about ships. I have heard seamen ascribe human properties to them; I have heard them compared to women for their beauty and their meanness; and, according to that shipmate aboard the little schooner, all kinds of sexual pleasure may even be had from them. The furthest I will go on this tack is to give them the feminine pronoun, for in so far as they are big rounded bodies under constant movement I believe they deserve better than a neuter identity. When I served in French ships and had to scratch along with the French language I could never manage to remember where I was with my nautical pronouns.

'Elle est belle,' I would say to Jacquot, painting the hull alongside me, meaning the nice little craft entering the port.

'Qui, la poule là-bas?' he'd reply, coarsely questioning the virtue of the for all he knew innocent woman who had strayed along the quayside.

'Non, pas la poule, le bateau.'

'Le bateau est beau, la poule est belle'; he used to enunciate the forenoon lesson clearly and slowly, but I never could repeat it with certainty.

This ship I stood on now was at last without motion, no feel in her foredeck except of the wood in her fish-scarred planks; no soft vibration from the engine, not even the feel of the hum of her donkey, the little engine which provides the ship with her auxiliary power, her lighting and so on; not a spark of life or heat aboard, a dead neuter thing if ever there was one. I went quickly forward under the whaleback where we lived, collected all my gear in the uncomfortable darkness, threw it down on to a dry patch of the dock and hurried off her. She was nothing to do with me until they put her back in the water.

CHAPTER 5

# *The Ship's Runner*

Anyone who has served in foreign-going ships knows that the ship's runner is the chandler's assistant. His job is literally to run, on his legs or in a car, errands at the command of whoever is in charge of ship's stores. He is at the beck and call of the captain, the mate, the bosun, the chief engineer, the chief steward and anyone else who can work up enough authority. They all borrow his services as by right from the agent or chandler restocking the ship. I have known plenty of them and all were the most willing of men. They can usually be found somewhere on deck, in the waist of the ship within hail of the gangway, affably passing the time with whoever will bend on a yarn. There is apparently nothing they do not know about the port they work in, and they can put a fair price on anything, from a bit of stolen gear to the weight of the backhander which the custom's officer will want. They know where all the available women live and with all the understanding in the world will fix up a good run ashore. I have known only one who was not multilingual and he was in a frenzy to make a start on English. They are a set of men as devoid of vanity or false airs and graces as any you could think of. Their judgment is objective, friendly, and uncomplicated by questions of race or creed. Many of them are generous, most of them are pitifully rewarded both by their employers and by the seafarers they run about for, and not one I met had ever been or would ever go to sea.

Very different is the runner on the Fish Dock. In the first place he is usually an ex-bosun of a trawler who has 'worked himself ashore'. He has an office of his own just inside the public entrance of every trawling company, and his own runner, meaning a boy, to dash about for him. Far from being a more or less well-treated serf, he is a man of the greatest importance on the dock, a figure to be reckoned with by all trawlermen and by not a few skippers and mates. He derives his power (in the classic manner) from the shortage of berths and the abundance of men to fill them. He does various jobs in the supply department, but it is as master of the ship's official log book, in which the hands sign off and on, that he cracks his whip—and makes his fortune.

In all my years at sea, in all the different sorts of ship I had served in, I had never once paid for a berth, for the privilege of toiling afloat, in fact I had never heard of such deals. When I did hear of them I did not believe the tale, and when the fact was proved to me I swore that I for one would offer no such bribes. But spiky affectations of honour such as this were soon smoothed away when at a later date I had to put up with unemployment myself. Indeed at the end of my first 'rest' I was only too anxious to find a runner who would condescend to accept my promise of cash on settling day. And when I settled at the end of that trip the very furthest thing from my mind was the thought of welshing. I paid, and like many trawlermen I sweetened my account with runners at the end of every trip, whether I was sacked or whether I wasn't. I do not say that these bribes are paid by every trawlerman on the dock. There were some whose ability was so complete that even among this élite of seafarers, the trawler crews of the Hull Fish Dock, men without question not to be equalled by the crews of any other class of ship, they, by their superiority among us, could always command a place in the fo'c's'le. If these men happened to take a month ashore it would indeed be because they were resting, not sacked; and when they decided in their own good time to go back, a few days' notice to the runner, given in a fairly lordly way, would always see them shipped in one of the latest vessels, commanded by a skipper who could almost guarantee a rich pay-off. But these, so to speak, were the first among equals, and there were few of them. Others who did not have to find a backhander for the runner were those who could claim a close relationship with someone influential in a ship or on the dock, perhaps even with a runner himself. If a likely young hand had the sense to marry say, a skipper's daughter, then among the ships which that skipper and his skipper friends commanded there would always be a berth for him to climb into, and things being the way they are in this world no sensible argument can be put up against that. But yet others I knew, and these were famous on the dock, who were such masters of the art of ingratiating themselves that they too paid no bribes, or paid less than most.

The majority of us, though expert seamen, were by no means super-trawlermen, nor were we related to the best of trawling families. As there were so many more of us than there were jobs, it came to this: if you wanted to ship you had to pay, and runners got rich.

Now I am not going to complain, or to be jealous, at the thought of an ex-trawler bosun, perhaps with twenty-five years at sea in his log book, reclining peacefully as the owner of the best of houses in the neatest suburb, digesting three meals a day, with a belly full of free beer for him whenever he feels inclined to walk into a trawlerman's public house, taking at least eight hours' sleep in every twenty-four, and all this for not much more than a day labourer's pay. On the contrary, far from complaining, I am all for the comfortable retirement of good men when they have put their time in; when they decide at last to go ashore I am all for someone providing them with good employment which does not exhaust them. But what I, and many other fishermen wish, is that this pleasant life could be arranged without subscriptions from men still afloat. And what of the bosuns who finally climb ashore after not twenty-five, but thirty-five and even forty years of wringing salt water out of their mufflers? What of them, if there are not enough runner's jobs to go around?

The day I first walked on to the Fish Dock I knew nothing of all this corruption. I came up the ramp from under the railway bridge and on to the dock by the entrance near the lock basin, making for one of the two big companies which had their offices at this end of the dock on the short wall. It was by now about a quarter to eleven, the right time for business for unemployed sea-farers.

# CHAPTER 6

# *The Log Book*

A group of twenty-five or more men were standing about on the cobbled roadway between the company offices and the dock edge. From time to time a man detached himself from the group and strolled off up the dock, while others joined. To the newcomer the greeting was a 'Now then, Bill', or a 'Now then, Joe', in a tone which was friendly enough but yet carried a sort of challenge.

'Is this Steer's?' I asked one of the men.

'Aye.' He was slight and short with a shock of soft black hair. His voice was rough and very deep for such a little man.

'I want the shipping office.'

'You mean the runner's office.' He had me weighed up as a man in need of a berth and looked at me with open curiosity, for I was an obvious stranger there. At that moment a taxi drove past just behind my back. I sensed something coming and jumped aside but was far too late to get out of the way of the full muddy puddle which the cab sloshed over my trousers. I felt the cold muck running down my legs and into my shoes. A laugh went up and those who saw it were quick to tell the others what had happened.

'Did she drop one on you?'

'Are you all wet, mate?'

Then a man stepped out of the building and everyone was quiet. He looked us over and then beckoned with an eye and a finger. The little man next to me pushed to the front.

'You mean me, Johnny?' he called out, but the man was back in the building.

'Aye, you. Get in there,' someone said.

'Borrow my fountain pen.'

Someone else said, 'The bastard's icing me back. I've been out three weeks longer than Punch.'

The crowd settled back again and a man near me said, 'You

might be all right, Harry. The bosun told me she wants three hands and a snacker.'

The man called Harry nodded at the doorway. 'Aye, but I'm not favourite with that bastard in there.'

In a few minutes the dark little man came through the door.

'There's ink on his finger,' a man shouted.

'Aye, Punch, you'll be happy in her. Only the best of men sign with him.'

The little man went shyly along the road off the dock, and there was a guffaw or two, not quite good-natured, then silence as the runner stood again in his doorway.

'No decky learners here?' he said.

There was no reply. Now decky learner was the lowest rating among the part of a trawler crew that works the trawl, namely the fishermen as opposed to the engineers, firemen, trimmers, cooks, galley-boys and radio operators. These were the ship's lads, aged usually between sixteen or seventeen and nineteen or twenty. I pushed to the front. Someone said, 'Is that a decky learner?'

'Aye, he's an old decky learner.' The speaker rolled out the word 'old' until the syllable weighed me down with years. I followed the runner into the office. Someone laughed.

'You're in, mate.'

'Who's that?' a man asked.

Inside, the office was small. There were two other doors leading, it seemed, into the main building. The only furniture was a high desk, such as ledger clerks used to sit behind on tall stools, and two hard, straight chairs. On the desk the big pages of a ship's official log book were spread open. The runner stood by the desk, leaning an elbow on it and faced me as I came in.

'Where are you from, son?'

'I've come over from Australia.'

'Have you been fishing before?'

I took out from an inside pocket a wallet of papers. Some were legal looking documents heavily franked with the stamps of foreign consulates; others were no more than scraps of paper, briefly recording a single short trip. The whole history of my seafaring was written down in those papers, for I had carefully preserved my record from every ship. I had never been a 'company's man', that is a man who committed his career to one company, voyaging steadily towards a pension, a little supplement to add to what the government pays old men. On the contrary, I had freelanced, been prepared to ship in any company of any country. Therefore paper was always of the first importance to me. It got me over the difficulties of introduction, made way for social niceties in those foreign ports where the police and immigration officials are only too inclined to take poor seamen in need of ships for criminals. The runner turned over every leaf, reading it all carefully.

'I see you was in a trawler out of Sydney. It says you went third hand.'

'Yes.'

'And you want a start as decky learner?' He turned his head to the log book, then looked at me, and then put his attention back to my papers. He was a burly man, easily filling out his stained old suit. Over his round face a cap was set, square and flat. His voice was quiet, but remembering the effect of the sight of him on the men outside it was clear that he seldom had to raise it. The hands, turning over the story of my life, were fat with well-cared for, clean, finger nails, strong, dark coloured and trimmed just before they curved over his finger tips.

'You're a bit old to go snacker.'

'Twenty-six.'

He thought my comment over, taking time to make up his mind. There was no way for me to tell what difficulties there were in shipping me, but had I known him as well as I knew him a year later I would have been able to guess. He was probably calculating my lack of friends in Hull ships, my uncertain ability to put up with trawler conditions out of the Hull Fish Dock, and my chance of finally emerging as a trained hand, more or less permanently employed by Steer's. What these variables came down to was how much a year, from my pay packet, were we worth to one another?

'You can sign,' he said at last. He asked me the usual details— name, place of birth, next of kin, and filled the information into

(*right*) One of the great iron-shod trawl doors with a view of the gallus

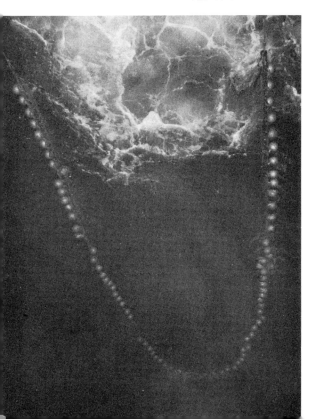

(*left*) Giant iron beads or bobbins, called the dan lenos

*Page 34* (*above*) Hauling in the net off Iceland; (*below*) hauling in the net in rough weather—a view of the rope which drags the net on board

the columns in a clear, careful hand. He handed me the pen and I scratched in my signature, thus at the same time completing an identity and committing myself to the laws governing ships, voyages and crews.

I have never enjoyed this ceremony of 'taking the pen', for I do not see the need of special laws to float by, and I never met a seaman who did. This is not to say that there are no mutinously inclined men at sea, nor men who would not like to cut a captain's throat as soon as he told them to let go the mooring ropes. There are no doubt as many hard-case human beings afloat, in proportion, as there are ashore, but if the ordinary laws are enough for them on the land, why must there be so much more abiding by laws—meaning law enforcement—when it comes to going to sea? The fact is that the laws under which seamen labour have been rigged over the years by shipowners themselves. Show me the seaman who feels morally bound, before setting off, to put his name to a document which is there solely to remind him of the penalties for 'refusing to obey a command' and so on. No, it's not us who need the laws but them, the shipowners. The sort of log book I would like to see, for a change, would be one where the owner has to sign himself into my hands; a log book where it is written down that not only does he have to repatriate me when I am sick and provide me with a few other meagre benefits to do with food and leisure, signifying that he does at least admit I am alive, but more than that, I want to see his signature promising to pay me, under the penalty of his being imprisoned or fined (whichever goes hardest with him), wages sufficient for the upkeep of wife, children and widowed mother, wages sufficient to give me a good run ashore whenever I need one, and a fund for a comfortable pension to be put at my disposal before I am too old to enjoy it. Further he should undertake that toil shall be light, entertaining, and not too long drawn out, that I do not take unjustifiable risks with my life by venturing in his ships, and lastly promise to feed me as well as he feeds himself. They say this is the official log book which you find on the bridge of ships in the Hope Line, but I never had the luck to float in one of theirs.

There is one advantage in signing on. Once your name is in the log book you are immediately back in the ranks of respectably employed, meaning that you can get credit.

'I need some money to square up ashore,' I said to the runner. That was no problem now. He filled out a slip which stated that I was shipped in the rating of decky learner aboard the steam trawler *Steerwell*, and told me to take it up to the cashier.

'Now don't let me down, son.' An odd thing to say, I thought, and wondered about the position held in the company by this man. Was my employment in some way dependent on his good opinion? It was a question which was answered on settling morning at the end of my first trip.

Meanwhile I put it out of my mind and went up the stairs to the cashier. In a partition built across a bare room was a glass-fronted door and a sliding panel at chest height. On the glass in the panel was stencilled the words: 'Cashier. Knock and wait'. I knocked, I could hear the sounds of the clerks moving about behind the partition, talk, and the noise of a tremendous typewriter which clanged at the end of each line and whose carrier, at this signal, was crashed back ready for the next. I continued to wait then knocked again. Someone inside shouted, 'Wait!' I sat down on a wooden bench stretching along one of the walls. No different then, in this office from any other shipping office, I thought; shipping clerks must be an international race, a universal type diseased with rudeness. I passed the time remembering a ship I paid off in Cardiff. We had a glass or two on the way to the office, no more than enough to be friendly, and all would have been well if the clerk had not made an error in manners.

'Sign here,' he said, and turned the cash book round to face the man in front of me at the cubby-hole.

'Where, here?' said my shipmate, a powerful man, looking along the entries in the ledger.

'There; can't you read?'

The paid-off man put down the pen, gave the ledger to me, and took the clerk by the lapels of his coat. His big fingers closed over tie, shirt, and no doubt took in a cubic inch or two of the flesh of the man's chest. Carefully he drew him through the hatch. Some of the beading surrounding it split away. The face of the cashier, twisted sideways on his neck by the strength of the grip he was in, was frightened; his eyes were wide open.

'Come here, one of you,' said the seaman to the two officials remaining inside. One hurried to the counter.

'Give your mate my lay, will you. That's it, that one there.'

The money in its envelope was passed through, and put by my friend into the hand of the scared man he was holding up. It seemed to be in no one's mind, neither among us nor among the functionaries, to try to stop what was taking place.

'Open the book, will you.' I opened it on the counter.

'Now where do I have to sign, then?'

'Sign there, Mr Johnson, please.' The clerk, released, pointed at the appropriate column and carefully handed over the money.

I had just signed on, however, which meant that my state of mind was very modest. I was in no mood to show impatience. I waited for about ten minutes more and was just considering another discreet knock, not to rouse them to the hatch, exactly, but simply to let them know that I was still there, when it banged open and a man said, 'What do you want?'

'Can you give me a sub, please?' His hand appeared and I put into it the slip given me by the runner.

'Three pounds.'

'Can't you make it five, mister?'

'No, can't do it. Three pounds for a decky learner.'

No point in arguing. This was obviously the regulation. I signed his pay sheet, took the money and made off. As I was leaving the building a thought suddenly struck me and I turned back to the runner's office. But at that moment he stepped outside, and on a blackboard mounted in the wall of the building, chalked in his neat hand: '*Steerwell*. Wednesday, 3.30 am.'

'He means tomorrow morning,' said one of the men still standing there. 'Don't get left on the dock, mate.'

# CHAPTER 7

# Pine's, Noon

I went back under the tunnel and through the avenue. Turning into the Hessle Road I passed Pine's, the big public house pointed out to me on my way to the dock, and with three pounds comfortably in my trouser pocket I decided I could afford a drink. The doorway alongside me had a sign over it, 'Room', and I went in past a group of idlers chatting on the pavement.

At the end of a short, brown-painted, dirty corridor with the 'men's' leading off it was an open door; inside was 'Pine's Room'. The colour of the walls from four feet above the floor to the ceiling was a thin blue-green reflecting what little daylight filtered through the grimy street windows; below was the same brown paint as in the corridor. In spite of two big globes suspended from the ceiling in support of the worn-out daylight, the room looked as though the only way to make it warm and cheerful would be to draw curtains across the windows, finish with daylight altogether and flood it with artificial light.

There was no decoration on the wall, except where above the door someone had painted a design of a garden trellis through which the poor likeness of a few roses twined, drab and faded from tobacco smoke. The only life in the room was in a corner to the right of the door, where under a shallow wooden canopy a bar with a wide mahogany counter had been cut through the wall. This was aglow with light coming from some other part of the house which must have been bright. Five or six men were there drinking large glasses of dark beer. In the centre of the room were three or four tables with straight-backed chairs around them. Along its sides were more tables and chairs; and benches with wooden backs and armrests were fitted close up to the walls. There was room for about eighty to sit down. But at that moment there were only one or two pairs of men sitting talking at the side tables with glasses of the dark beer before them and near the bar two young women, sitting beside one another on a bench, upright and silent, gazing patiently at long-stemmed glasses of drink placed on their table. At the opposite end of the room was a platform built about eight or ten inches above the floor on which was a piano covered carelessly with a cloth, a big juke-box with its rack of records and its working parts displayed under a coloured floodlighting device inside the casing, a drum and a microphone on a tall chromium stand. Two big columns which supported the ceiling, one in each half of the room, were encased, between five and eight feet above the bare floor, with a mosaic of tiny tinted mirrors worked into the cylindrical surfaces. As one moved, they flashed and glittered even in that poor light.

I went to the bar to buy my drink and there in the corner saw the dark little man who had signed in the *Steerwell* before me.

'Did you get shipped?' he asked.

'Aye.'

'I told the runner when I was in the office there was a new snacker outside needing a start.'

'How did you know I wanted a start?' I said.

'I'm not as daft as I look. I knew you was a stranger. You don't look like an engineer. You can't be an operator else you wouldn't be looking for work on the Fish Dock, so you had to be a deckie, and everybody out of Hull starts as decky learner, see.' I nodded.

'The lads were a bit hard on you, weren't they?' I remembered the guffaws as he went off the dock.

'No, mate, you don't want to worry about that. I know most of those men. Some of them's been ashore too long, that's all. I've floated with most of them, see. They're all right.' He told me that he had been ashore three weeks, sacked with five others from his last ship, and now he counted himself lucky to be first back. His shipmates might have two or three weeks more walking about in front of them.

'Those spare hands outside the office was just getting a bit edgy,' he said. 'It sharpens you up nicely when you've been standing around for ten days or more.' He looked at me with a grin. 'I wonder why that bastard put me back so quick. Maybe he thinks I've got a little bit saved up.'

'Do you often get sacked, then?'

'Depends if your face fits. Last ship I did eleven trips. First nine was a doddle, we had a daddy of a skipper and he made us a bob or two. Then they unshipped him, see. The new man wants his inner circle with him, so me and the other four gets done.' He finished off his beer and looked about. 'Bastard of a place, Pine's Room, in the middle of the day. Never anyone in here till near bagging-off time.'


Pine's 'Bar' was a different world. It was brilliantly illuminated by daylight through big windows in two of the walls, and by plenty of massive light globes hanging from the ceiling. The room was divided lengthways by a fine counter which was set off the inside wall some 8 feet, thus forming a snug little corner at one of its ends and a natural lead out to a curtained street exit at the other. Behind this counter was the usual wooden shelf architecture, with curved decoration, varnished and polished, containing a great stock of drink. In the topmost shelves were the bottles of rare liquor, all kinds of strong alcohol, placed up there, I used to think, only in case drinkers wanted to make special launchings into seas of drunkenness. There were notices around the bar advertising firms of taxis who were prepared to send cars to meet any tide, day or night. Two other notices were exhortatory: 'Fishermen. We stock the famous "Sir James's Rum". Take a bottle with you to sea', and hanging in the centre of the shelves was a decorated board with the statement 'your credit is good in here' drawn in pokerwork above the picture of a finger pointing into the rectum of a pig. There was a crowd of men standing at the bar and a number of others sitting on benches around the walls.

Punch pushed his way to the counter and called out in his big voice to one of the barmaids who were the only women in the room. She served two glasses of the dark beer which nearly everyone was drinking.

'Better in here,' he said. 'You can see a few of the lads in the bar. All hands gets in here when they come off the dock.'

'Is everyone in here off the trawlers?'

'Aye, just about.' He looked round. 'Some of them's finished with it now, and some of them's bobbing. But they've nearly all been at it one way or another.' He faced me. 'What've you come up here for?'

I told him about the trawlers working out of Sydney and about what I had heard of Hull. I asked him about the money earned by Hull men.

'All depends on the market,' said Punch. 'You'll find out how the bastards work that. But if you're going snacker you'll pick up about three pounds ten in the thousand. That means if we dock and make five thousand for the trip your lay'll be near sixteen notes, plus your wages, plus your liver money, less your tax, bond and the price of your gear. I'll tell you something, son, they don't give the bastard away. You might pick up twenty-five pound for a three-week voyage. Let's get 'em in again.' He pushed back to the bar. 'You can buy 'em when we get ashore after this one.'

There was plenty of noise in the bar for everyone seemed to be talking; a few of the voices were raised from time to time almost to a shout, while a surge of laughter constantly broke over the conversations. As far as I could hear the talk was of fishing, the points made in a brusque, laconic way, much of it expressed in a technical language which I could barely follow, and all filled with an idiom taken from the deck and from the gear of the ships they worked in. As Punch returned to the bar a man spoke to him.

'Now then, Punch. Are you drinking with us poor unemployed spare hands, then?' The speaker was a heavy bald-headed man whose mouth, with no teeth in it, wide, with the lips turned in over his gums, was carved across his face far back between the big promontories of nose and chin. There was plenty of flesh over the large area between jaw and forehead. He was clean shaven, exposing the deep pore structure of his skin. He stood with his back to the bar, holding his beer across his belly. He looked at Punch, raised his glass and poured the beer down his throat.

'Have a pint then, Willy,' said Punch and handed to the drinker one of the two glasses he was carrying. The man he had called Willy accepted the glass and raised it to Punch's back, but he was already pushing to the bar for a replacement.

'Too much hurry,' Willy affirmed. 'Never any time for manners. You see what I mean, we've not even been properly introduced.' His eyes were alert, moving swiftly about behind the ample eyelids. I nearly missed the flicker of a wink he signalled at me. Punch came back.

'Are you just ashore, Willy?'

'From my winter cruise, yes. Ahead lie cruises I will take in spring and summer, and a little run off in the autumn. They permitted me to board the *Shelley*.' He turned earnestly to me. 'A famous poet, you know, after whom this good ship was named.' He raised his glass solemnly and drank off all the beer in it. 'It gives me the greatest pleasure to inform you that we made six thousand pounds. I am therefore able to ask you to join me in more refreshment.'

'Nay, Willy, have another with us.' But the big man had moved swiftly to the bar.

Punch turned to me. 'He's a right old bastard, is Willy,' he said quietly. 'There isn't a man on the dock wouldn't buy him a beer, and most of them would do a lot more. But he won't have it. He used to be one of the best of hands but they've spragged him. They said he was a ringleader of the strike we had here. We was ashore a long time and we didn't do any good. But when we went back the gaffers said it was all going to be forgotten. No victimisation, they said. But they've only given Willy four trips a year since then. Christmas, Easter, Whitsun and August, when nobody else wants to float.'

Willy came back with two glasses of beer and two measures of rum all held neatly between his big capable-looking hands. He returned to the bar for his own. Punch looked over at one of the tables where there were spare seats. 'May as well sit down if Willy's out for a dram or two.' We settled into seats.

'Ah,' Willy said, stepping firmly to the table, 'I see you have decided to drop a buoy, as they say in our industry. They tell

42

me a little rum is just the thing for warming the heart of an old
sailor.' He turned to Punch and lowered into a seat. 'You've not
introduced me to our young friend, Punch. Is anything the
matter with him? Is he a German?'

Punch recounted the events of the morning.

'Yes, news came to me that a man or two is hanging about on the
dock.' He leaned at me. 'Listen, mate, don't be daft.' The eye suddenly glittered at me; no longer amiable, the character of the big
face changed, strong muscles made the flesh hard and tough; the
flowered speech was gone. 'Go away. You better leave Hull.
Trawling's the biggest bastard in England. You'll finish up like
our shipmate, Punch here, or any other of the poor bastards in
this bar. I'll tell you what, they spend three-quarters of their life
swilling about in the Frozen North and the other quarter trying
to talk their way past bastard ship's runners. You look all right
now, but you'll be a slave in a year. Talk out of turn and you'll
be spragged. Get a little bit tired and you'll be spragged. Don't
suck up to the skipper and you'll be spragged. Call the mate a
bastard and you'll be spragged. Get on the wrong side of the
inner circle and they'll have you out of her. Tell the old man you
don't want to tow in a bleeding gale and you'll have to get your
rags off her when you dock. And when you can't jump about quite
as fast as you used to you'll find you'll be doing a trip when
nobody else wants to go. In the end they'll push you out of it
altogether. And then what d'you think you'll do? I'll tell you.
Some of the rendered down old deckies come into Pine's and do
a bit of fishing with a pint in front of 'em while they're waiting
for a backhander from the lads, if they're lucky. They scratch a
living off the dock as best they can, a little bit in the shore gangs,
a little bit on the market, a little bit of bobbing if they know the
right somebody, see. There's others you never hear about. They
just go. Nobody wants 'em any more, so they go. Is that right,
Punch?'

'Don't be like that, Willy. You know the game.'

Willy put his dram to his lips and drank the measure as though
he was biting it from the glass. Then he sat back in his chair.

'I beg your pardon. For a moment I forgot myself.' He resumed the grand manner. 'The Fish Dock, as you will in time discover, is a benefit society run by the kind co-operation of trawler owners and fish merchants for the physical and moral welfare of poor fishermen who do not know the value of money, and only get drunk when they earn too much.'

'Let's get some more in,' said Punch. I stood up but met the full stare of Willy's commanding eye.

'Sit down, young man. Respect the company you are in. When Punch has spent his modest resources he will let you know.' I put my money back in my pocket and sat down.

# CHAPTER 8

# *Departure*

Twice in twenty-four hours I had been told to keep clear of the trawlers. No doubt the reasons for the advice were different; as different as those two human beings, Willy and my landlady, were different. But the result was the same—get away.

The views of the landlady could be discounted. Men like me could expect little but short shrift from women like her. We didn't show sign enough of virtue (meaning money) for them to waste sympathy on us.

'I'd like to square up with you now,' I said, 'I'm leaving at three in the morning.'

'You're late for your supper,' she countered, opening the bargaining. 'It's ready for you in the kitchen. You'll have to see the Captain about your bill.'

It was cold in the street and I needed the bed they were lending me for another four hours, so I followed her into the kitchen. The Captain was sitting by the stove; the parrot was on the table. They both looked at me as I entered.

'Where've you been? My wife cooked your supper for you, on the table there.'

It was only half true. Near the edge of the big unlaid table was a plate containing a piece of fish and some chips, not cooked by her but all boiled hours before in the deep fat of a fish shop cooker. No doubt the woman had kept the meal waiting for me a while in her oven, but it had been removed some time before and by the look of it had gone cold. However, I was hungry and sat up to the table. She started confidently. Counting the parrot, the odds were three against one; I could see that I was in for some hard dealing.

'Now then, that's two nights bed, breakfast—it was a shame to waste that good food—and two suppers.'

45

As she said it the first mouthful of the crust of the fried batter in which the fish was wrapped broke between my teeth. A damp sog, like fibrous jelly, spread over my tongue. My throat filled immediately, brimming with the rum and beer drunk during the day. I clamped my lips and convulsed the throat muscles with the effort to swallow everything. Only the determination to get the financial better of these two, to cut the profit from their avarice even by half-a-crown, prevented me vomiting. They would have me if I let that throatful come up.

'Wait while I eat this,' I breathed out carefully.

I believe the three of them knew what I was suffering. I must have been pale and I could feel sweat all over me. It was cruel to be sitting there, steadily masticating and swallowing, one mouthful ahead of nausea, cruel that a man about to go to sea should have to eat meals like this on his last two nights ashore. I got angry.

'What did you cook me for my breakfast?' I was able to manage a firm voice. She hesitated. Was it her memory, or had she cooked nothing? She glanced at the parrot, and I laid my bet.

'I think a pound would cover it all.'

She hesitated again, too long, and I picked up my winnings; that is, I placed a note on the table in front of the bird. No one spoke. I pushed away a nearly clear plate and, almost in control of myself, looked at her. Sweet to turn the knife in this sort of wound.

'What about a cup of tea then, now that's over.' Now what's over, the supper or the bargaining—what did I mean? There was no way for her to find out. She looked from me to the Captain, but help was not to be had from him. The ground had shifted too quickly. He kept his eyes steadfastly on the stove. The parrot moved sideways across the table, an inch or two nearer the money. She screwed her mouth up, rose to her feet, smoothed a fold from the hip of her dress, and shooshed the bird off the table. He let out the beginnings of a screech and flapped on to his perch where he sat, moving his head about on his skinny neck stretched clear of the body feathers; an angry bird. I forecast an ugly five minutes for the parrot and the Captain when she had them alone. She put the money in her dress pocket and fussed at the stove with the kettle and tea-pot.

'I'll be full up when you come back from sea,' she said with spite, 'you'll have to find somewhere else to live.' The last harmless round of her ammunition. I stretched out in my chair, made a cigarette, and sipped my cup of tea.

What Willy had said about the trawlers was a different matter; it deserved very careful thought. As long as I stayed ashore I was committed to nothing. My signature in the log book was simply my mark on a sheet of paper, a mere matter for discussion, between police, trawler owners and myself in the magistrate's court. But afloat and fishing? The question asked for concentration. I said good night, and went up to my attic.


It was sleeting as my taxi turned into the avenue but I noticed in the dark two more making their way to the dock. We followed behind them under the tunnel and on to the cobbled entrance. The driver looked back at me.

'Do you want the stores?' he said.

Punch had told me what gear was needed and I got out to buy it when he stopped on the dock at the rear of a number of waiting cars.

Up a lane, in among the buildings near the lock basin, was a dimly lit doorway flanking a shop window, empty save for a stack of woollen clothing and a brief display of waterproof gloves. There was a crowd of men round the shop entrance and inside it was full. Some of the men were pressed along the length of the interior of the shop window.

'D'you want to get through, mate?' said one of them, making room for me to pass him.

'It's all right, after you,' said I, equally polite.

He looked at me. 'Are you fresh on the dock, mate? Go on, go through.'

Without understanding him I took my place in one of the three queues waiting before a long, broad mahogany counter. Behind the counter clerks in dustcoats attended the men standing in front.

47

For sale were all kinds of seafaring clothing, but in particular the special trawler gear; magnificent rubber thigh boots; 'frocks', that is buttonless overalls which enveloped a man from neck to knees, made of rubberised canvas or plastic; 'fearnoughts', which are white loose-fitting trousers made of a good thick blanket material with seamen's flaps instead of flybuttons; 'smocks', strong cotton blouses without buttons worn under the frock; thick jerseys made from wool containing its natural oils, known as 'abb'; underwear made either from light wool, or for those cold-blooded hands who needed a little something extra of warmth, from a thick, pink wool as heavy as abb. Then there were mittens, gutting gloves, either in cotton or rubber, and excellent single-bladed jack-knives, known as 'gutting knives', sold in two sizes to fit your own gutting style and the size of your hand. I saw some of the men supplied with the comfortable slip-on shoes, suitable for watchkeeping on the bridge and common aboard all classes of ship; others bought handsome leather tobacco pouches, and everyone bought at least two ounces of a kind of cigarette tobacco wrapped in blue paper. This was the famous 'Trawler-man's Punch', not seen on sale anywhere except around the Fish Dock, a special shag which I, for one, never found bettered. It was strong, it did not make you cough, it was easy to roll and it used to burn beautifully.

Some of the men bought five or six packets of Punch, and it was then that I saw the purpose of those standing along the window. They were on 'Tobacco Road'. As the purchasers made their way to the door some of them pressed an ounce into the hand of a man waiting. One or two of these beneficiaries made off, but others stood by and took a considerable toll of shag from the men off to sea.

I discovered later that some of these men were well-known cadgers, ex-trawlermen who added their take from Tobacco Road —converted into cash—to whatever else they could amass for a living. I came to know one or two of them. Characteristically they were jesters with a talent for raising a laugh at the expense of someone who, for an unwary moment, had left himself un-guarded. So sharp were the tongues of some of them that, in

48

spite of their flagrant beggardom, they were given a grudging respect, and it was accepted that they had established a right to the tax they levied, to the 'pitches' which they 'worked'. Not that these wits were lazy; after all it needs effort to be ready, at any state of the tide, to originate comment caustic enough to earn a dividend. Moreover, for the trawlermen who had a spark or two of life in them on a cold sailing morning (those who had a bottle of rum in their bags) the jesters would sometimes, for a favour as it were, act as bag carriers. They could then be seen, passing the last half-hour before the ship left, drinking up their share of liquor in the fo'c's'le as invited guests. But it must be noted that once aboard the ships, even with a dram glass in the hand, their wit was less ready; it was as though they admitted that their licence extended only to the edge of the dock and no further. On the fo'c's'le of a trawler about to leave on a tide they used to play their role with discretion, for such jests as were necessary at that grim moment could safely be left to the crew. And when the time came for letting go the ropes they did no more than wish us a cheerful farewell—until they stepped off her.

I knew one of these Tobacco Road clowns who, after he had made his goodbyes and had jumped back on to the dock and had straightened himself up, seemed visibly to need to recover his wit and spirit. Once his feet were in contact with the stability of dry land, and the faintest fraction of a chance that he would be shanghaid had vanished (there is the awful fear, not quite buried in the back of an ex-seaman's mind, that his visit of goodwill aboard a departing ship may result in the horrible circumstances that, by mistake, he leaves with her; I take, myself, the greatest care to get ashore in good time), to show us what he thought of ships and the sea, he used to dance three or four steps of a crazy and satirical hornpipe. But at the same time, to show that he was on the side of us in the fo'c's'le and against the man on the bridge, he used to raise two fingers and make a set of coarse gestures in the direction of the bridge windows. He then used to shamble away in the imitation of a drunk, raising and drinking imaginary glasses to our success.

'Daft bastard,' someone would say.

'Aye, but he works a bloody good pitch on Tobacco Road.'

But by far the majority of the men were not waiting there as casuals but to say goodbye to a particular friend and to receive from him the gift of an ounce or two of Punch. They were on the dock because they were badly out of work. They needed the tobacco, and they needed the livener of a dram in the fo'c's'le, even if it meant turning out at three o'clock on a winter's morning when the breeze finds all the cracks in shore clothing. They were there not only to see the departure of an old friend in a ship but to reassure themselves that sooner or later they too would be shipped. Another reason was that the friend they were sending off they would perhaps not meet for a year or more, for even though the length of a voyage was not more than twenty-one days, and usually less, their chance of coinciding ashore was a long one. Men with strong mutual affections, then, would often arrange to meet on the dock on sailing morning simply to spin their encounter out. So much the better if there was an ounce of Punch and a few drams of rum in it.

The stores clerk asked me my name and ship and I proceeded to fit myself out. The transaction was done on credit. You bought anything you needed almost without limit, signed a docket listing the new gear, and the total was deducted from your settlement at the end of the trip. Now a well-rigged trawlerman needed gear to the value of £25 if he was stripped right down to nakedness, and was to be fitted out for a winter voyage to the east end of the White Sea, say, or Bear Island, or the north-west side of Iceland. Most men 'worked' two pairs of boots and two frocks because of the condensation which collected inside them owing to the body's heat. Some who were frightened of 'Arthur' (arthritis) used to change boots and frock every two or three hours, but nearly all hands shifted their top-gear at least twice during the day and aired the wet stuff over the engines in the ship's driving room. These changes alone, essential to good health, absorbed about £14. On top was expenditure on gutting gloves and mittens for the protection of the hands, never less than about 24s a trip. Sou'westers, smocks, jerseys, underclothing and so on had to be kept in good order; in fact, when a man was

(*right*) The cod ends in sight

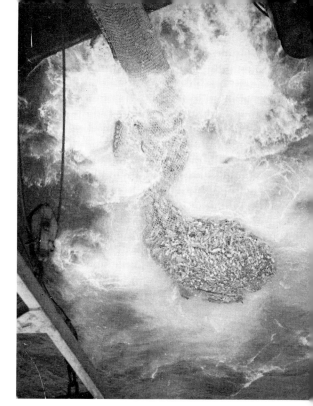

(*below*) Preparing to land the cod ends. A good catch

Page 52
(*left*) Another load aboard.
The men waiting

(*right*) Untying the knot to
release the fish from the cod
ends

going steadily in a ship, the cost of keeping himself properly protected from the weather and from the everyday hazards of the job, such as frostbite and torn fingers and hands, was more than 30s a week.

Of course the world being an expensive place to live in, certain hands used to go to sea 'schooner rigged'—one of the differences between a schooner and a square-rigged vessel is that the schooner needs less canvas to drive her. These were the men who would rather freeze and soak than pay the perpetual cost of gear.

I remember an old shipmate, called Ben, who did not believe in wasting his means in the stores. He used to wear the most amazing worn-out wrecks of frocks and boots. He used to rig himself so that he had one good side to face the weather, a sound boot which he wore to the breeze and the sea, and a holed boot for his lee side. The rips in his frock he would try to arrange under the lee of his armpit and what could not be tucked out of sight he used to lace up with twine. He was always damp but used to dry off as best he could by spending an occasional few minutes sitting in the drying-room with bottle and a dram glass.

I was in a ship once with Ben when he passed the days running off to the fishing grounds with his face fixed in a smug and secret look.

'What the bloody hell's up with him?' asked the bosun.

'You'll know soon enough,' said Ben with a smirk. We started fishing in due course and Ben, at the ready, appeared on deck. 'How do I look?' he said.

'What d'you mean, "how do I look"? Ugly as—Christ, look at him!'

Ben stood before us in the miracle of a brand new frock, bright blue and gleaming. During the whole ten days' work he took extraordinary care of himself.

'Mind my frock,' he would say, stepping delicately clear of the rags in a wire splice, 'Only the best of men can afford gear like this.'

'For Christ's sake get it worn out,' the mate said.

'Who's going to buy me another?' Ben answered.

Twenty-five pounds was three times what I could afford and I

D 53

had to make do with only the one of each essential item. I signed the docket, thus committing, before we had caught a single fish, more than £7 of my settlement.

These stores bills were a case where money had begotten money. Some years ago the trawler owners formed themselves into an association for the more efficient exploitation of the industry. Instead of each owner doing his best as hitherto to drive his rivals into bankruptcy, they decided, intelligently, to run their ships for their mutual benefit. Of course it was first necessary for the expanding firms to crush and consume the defeated, after which Fish Dock profits could be divided between the smaller number of the surviving large companies. A fund was then set up by members of the new association to run the ancillary industries of the dock, such as ship repair, fish meal, trawler insurance and so forth, and the complete control of the dock was drawn into their hands. But it is not my purpose to put down the economics of this dealing except in so far as trawlermen themselves are affected, and the price of fish is controlled.

Now as a trawlerman you stubbed your toe continually against this almighty combination and always to your cash loss. The stores was merely one of the subtler methods by which they used to rob us. Three facts must be noted. In the first place the stores, though a credit shop, was in no way a risk for its management, for a trawlerman's bill there was a part of his settlement itself, marked down as a prime payment in the trawler owner's office. Thus the man's credit was guaranteed for it was no less than the trawler owner's association which owned and controlled the stores. Second, trawlermen are, as we shall see, among the worst paid men in the country and, it must also be said, are not noted for their providence. They are inclined to spend rapidly what money they earn. They are often 'clean'—can we, by the way, conversely say that rich men are 'dirty'? Thus a man in need of four or five pounds' worth of gear was unlikely to give his business to the few private shops off the dock which stocked trawler clothing; neither were these shops likely to give him credit which could not be absolutely redeemed before he got his hands on his lay. Hence, outside the stores, little business was done. It had a near monopoly. The third fact follows as night follows day, for in the tradition of monopoly the stores pushed up prices. Far from making a reduction by reason of their certainty of an ample market, the price of the gear they sold was at least as high as in the little retail shops off the dock, and for many items they were not above inflating it by a few shillings.

Incidentally, I knew a trawler owner who enjoyed going away once every summer in one of his own ships, 'pleasuring'. He was a very wealthy man indeed, a member naturally of the trawler owners' association, and thus deriving a small but assured part of his millions from the stores. Yet once, when we were fishing, this man wanted to come on deck to look us over, and no doubt also, to show us that he too was a good fellow. He then had the monstrous and shameful idea to borrow, from a hand of about his own build, the top-gear necessary to keep him dry. I leave it to the reader to define precisely the arrogant and self-confident insolence of that trawler owner.

'I'd like to've lent the bastard my gear,' said Ben when he heard about it later. That was a time when his own gear could not even be called leaky; it was in its ultimate stage before disintegration. Ben used to take the greatest pains to point out to us, in strong language, what a set of robbers was the stores.

'You're giving money to the bastards,' he would say, reviling some well-rigged hand. Certainly it was true that he could afford to bring away more rum in his bag than most of us.

I parcelled up the gear and returned to the waiting taxi. We drove through the sleet which swirled in and out of the headlights a hundred yards up the river side of the dock to where a pair of trawlers was tied up. The lighting on the dock was dim, no more than would be found in a street of poor houses, and nothing distinct could be made out of the hull or superstructure of the ships. But their deck lights were on and the lights leading to the bridge, which shed a glow a few feet up the funnel. A little pool of light was reflected on the dock wall from a port in the bow of the near one.

'*Steerwell*'s outside,' said the driver, 'wait while I give you a hand. Bastard of a night, eh?' But I let him stay in his warm driver's seat, paid him off and threw my bag down on to the near deck. The edge of the dock was iced and my shoe slipped on the gunwale of the ship as I reached my leg down to it. There was a coating everywhere of the slush ice which lay under the drifting sleet. I clambered on to the deck, picked up my bag and crossed her to the outside ship. The *Steerwell* had swung away to a gust blown straight between them leaving a three-foot gap. I waited until she nudged alongside then heaved myself and my bag aboard her.

# CHAPTER 9

# The Fo'c's'le

At the forward end of the foredeck is the 'whaleback'. This is the name given by trawlermen to the built-up part of the ship's bow. It is there she sometimes takes aboard a green sea when she is stemming the weather. That sea then rolls away over either bow and also cascades aft on to the foredeck where it runs off through the scuppers. If you had seen a whale breaking surface and rolling the water off itself, the etymology of the trawling term whaleback would be clear. In the *Steerwell* there were three doorways cut into the after end of the whaledeck with foot-deep coamings at their base to prevent water getting under it. The doors themselves, hooked back wide open, were of heavy steel with steel strap hinges welded on to them, and fixed so that they turned on solid pins welded on the lintels. The doors could be secured watertight with clamps.

I stepped over the coaming of the right hand door which was lit dimly from a source within. Inside there was a small passage and I shuddered as I came in from the deck, out of the freezing weather, and felt the heat. The small light showed me a closed wooden door at the end of the passage. I opened it and stepping over another coaming came into the fo'c's'le.

Its central furniture was a little upright stove set in a concrete hearth with an asbestos lagged chimney leading through the deck-head. It was almost vibrating with the intensity of the fire which had been built inside. The heat it gave off was terrific. The little room, constructed on the fore and aft axis of the ship, was in the shape of a cut-down triangle with its small end right in the ship's stem. Athwart, along the base of this triangle where I was now standing, was a pair of bunks amidships of the doorway. On the sides of the triangle were more bunks, three sets to the right and two to the left. Where the last pair of bunks should have been on the left side was a little compartment which was our minute bathroom. Wooden benches were ranged alongside the lower of each pair of bunks. The total area of the little room was not much bigger than the sitting room of a small house but it provided sleeping and washing space for ten men. At that moment six of them were sitting on the benches, their bags stacked around the matting-covered deck. Though it was a tight little space, yet it looked clean and bright and very cheerful. Four or five empty beer bottles stood in the fireplace and on a bench was an opened crate. One of the men moved up on his bench so that I could sit down.

The most delicate social function I know is to join a ship's company. I have never floated in the big crack ships of the ocean passenger trade where the crews are numbered in tens of dozens. I take it that you can slip aboard these great ships almost unobserved, find a spare berth, stow your gear and mingle anonymously with the mob on deck when the time comes to set about your work. I should think no one except your cabin mate would even know your name until the ship was three days out. And it would not make very much difference if, among the hands, there was a very wide range of ability. If the key men such as the bosun, the carpenter (who drives the anchor winch) and a few others know their job, then a big crew can afford to carry a dozen or so not very expert men. After all, one of the main jobs of a hand in that class of ship is to keep her clean and protected from the weather. Thus a minority can be found aboard whose best work is done with a deck scrubber and a paintbrush. I have known a number of men who have spent their time in these ships who though they carry the rating 'able seaman' are yet scarcely even capable of making a hitch seamanlike enough to hang themselves. This is by no means their fault and I am not making priggish criticisms of a small number of men who go to sea. No, the fact is that men who float only on these oceangoing giants never have the opportunity to learn their job thoroughly. There simply is not the call for the best class of seamanship aboard them.

In a freighter or a tanker the range of jobs is vast, and if my earlier definition of seamanship—namely the handling of heavy weights in bad conditions—is a good one, then enough variations on this theme must be dealt with in a day's work aboard them to stretch the ingenuity of that old sailor Ulysses himself. You must be on top of your job. Moreover, aboard such ships as these, run by owners noted in the main for meanness, the deck complement is never quite sufficient. The mate could always do with a hand or two more; and that, incidentally, is why British ships are among the dirtiest which go to sea. For, limited by the small amount of money he is allowed to spend, that unlucky officer is constantly locked in combat with his crew, struggling to get from them a fraction more work than he is entitled to. They, naturally, are equally determined to hold it back. Hence neither mate nor crew can afford the luxury of carrying a half-trained man. And hence also the new man, on joining such ships, must expect to stand up to a critical—though, as the politeness of seafarers demands, unspoken—estimation of his ability to carry his rating. Material is gathered from yarns about his former ships, voyages, cargoes, weather, mates, skippers and in some cases even his women. All this and more forms part of the first judgment of the new ship-mate. A close but discreet professional watch will be kept on his work about the deck as the ship is made ready for sea, and when the time comes to get under way no doubt someone will see how he takes a turn with a wire round the winch drum, and if a spring with some weight on it has to be moved from winch drum to bitts, someone will surely note the amount of skill he brings to his share of that neat and tidy operation. In the end and in most cases the verdict on his ability is favourable, and will be made known tacitly by transferring to him the total responsibility for his share of the ship's work. He and the crew, with these profes-sional judgments behind them, can then set about uninhibitedly weighing up one another as human beings, a field for research which gives much wider scope for dispute, whose results, far from being unspoken, are liable to be published in the most terse and expressive way. Needless to say, the unfortunate who falls short professionally, no matter how noble his human charac-teristics, is only able to beg his pardon and excuse himself about the deck, a sort of living cross and crown of thorns combined, humped on the shoulders of his mates. Why, even Socrates, if he had had to work his passage out of Piraeus, might have thought twice before embarking on a dispute with the hands.

Aboard the Hull trawlers things are different. In the first place the hand signs only for a voyage of twenty-one days or so. For all he knows, as she sets out on sailing morning, the skipper or the mate may clear him out as soon as she docks again.

'How many trips did you make in your last?' says someone to the new hand.

'Eleven,' he answers ruefully, 'one out and one back,' which is to say that employment is liable to be very temporary in comparison with the big boats. Furthermore by far the majority of the men who ship in Hull trawlers are Hull men, and a great number of these are Hessle Road men, that is men who live on or just off that famous street. Hence, with the high turnover among crews, and the narrow field which they are recruited, nearly all the crews are more or less known to one another. And if we take it that the level of skill in the job is, by its very nature, bound to be extremely uniform, then we can understand that when a new man drops his gear aboard the question of his ability is hardly raised. It is assumed he is capable in the rating he holds. We will see shortly how impossible it is for the crew to carry passengers; aboard a trawler, more than aboard any other class of ship, they are utterly out of place.

Only with real strangers, that is men who come from other parts than Hull and certainly men from other countries, does the question of professional judgment seriously arise. Not only that, but an extreme interest is taken in the reasons for his being aboard. Trawlermen are far from being fooled by what the ignorant say of them, meaning for example the run of the mill journalist and his like, who on the basis of a single trip as 'pleasurer' produce their hair-raising romances; nor are they taken in by the way the public, including many citizens of Hull, estimate their reputedly fabulous earnings. They know, and I came to know, that they are men exploited in the highest degree, living out their lives in that shadowy place where fatigue becomes a real and identifiable poison permanent in the mind and body. A stranger who voluntarily joins them is suspect. They can account for their own presence in the industry in all sorts of reasonable and common ways. But what of him? One young hand of about twenty-three (though he himself had voyaged time and time again, tens of thousands of miles, throughout the whole of the Atlantic Arctic, from Novaya Zembla in the east end of the White Sea to the dreadful grounds north-west of Cape Farewell in Greenland) could not believe I had come from Australia to join a ship out of Hull. He found those paltry few thousand miles an amazing distance. In his opinion I had taken a crazy and outlandish step. But suspect or not, criminal, escaped convict, deserter, bigamist, no matter what, here and now I was a man shipped for a voyage, and therefore deserved a dram and a bottle of beer.

'Get that down you,' he said. 'You'll feel better.'

At that moment the door opened and a big friendly looking man entered.

'It's the bloody mate,' someone said. 'D'you want a dram, Ernie?'

'Aye, I'll have one,' the big man replied and emptied the offered glass. Then he turned it upside down.

'Are you ready, then, lads? The man wants his ship in the river.'

# CHAPTER 10

# The Run-off

North and south of the estuary of the Humber is the flat alluvial coastline of Yorkshire and Lincolnshire. The river flows into the North Sea over a range of shoals which are constantly on the move as the tide scours out and shifts the mud about on this low seaboard. It is a dangerous estuary for mariners and they do not count themselves clear until they pick up the line of sea marks called the Bull, the Spurn and the Humber. We were on these marks more than an hour down river of the Fish Dock and the tide was well on the ebb. We passed the first within a few yards of it and in the grey light I could see the ebb boiling under its upstream side, making it lean back, and on its downstream side surging away in a seething pattern like a ship's wake, so that the big buoy with its superstructure of steel, built in open basket work, was like some strange ship under way into the river, stemming the ebb.

Beyond this mark we began to feel the north-easterly weather, and the ship rolled gently to the swell. A little water splashed through the leeside scuppers and light spray whipped over the weather rail. The gear, which in the dock was lying all about the deck, nets, wires, floats, baskets, new bobbins, twine, wooden needles and all the apparatus put aboard by the shore gang to replace what had been lost or worn out on her last trip, had all been stowed; the anchors had been secured, the hatches on the foredeck battened down and in that hour running off to the river mouth the ship had been made thoroughly ready for sea. Now there was nothing on deck which was not lashed fast. When we finished doing this we went forward into the fo'c's'le and while the mate sat with us and arranged the watches, keeping old friends together where it was possible, we had a glass or two more by the warmth of the stove. Shoregoing clothing was taken off

and stowed, bags were unpacked, and the men dressed themselves
for fishing. But on their feet they put cut-down, worn-out thigh-
boots of ankle height known as 'clumpers', or slip-on deck shoes,
for sea boots are not worn by trawlermen on the run to and from
the grounds unless the weather compels them. They are heavy and
tire the legs.

Dressed in the white clothing—some of the 'fearnoughts', that
is the blanket trousers, were no longer white around the top of
the thighs where they were unprotected by sea boots but almost
polished with fish oil and dirt worked into the material and impossible to wash out—the men looked ready for action. They
began to take on the colour of their proper and unique environment.

I believe it is true that 'clothes make the man', for after all they
have been developed to cover up deficiencies no less than to
keep us warm. They do not exactly construct him but they make
him seem what he is, and to some degree they show what he is,
or what he would like to be. Put a man in unsuitable dress, in
contravention to the fashion he follows, and you put him at a
disadvantage in his work. No doubt the wealthy act rightly when
they set about the making of large quantities of money in stripes,
lapels, and sharp creases, for the way things are they are unlikely
to succeed in any other uniform; and there is a repulsive sort of
intelligence shown by those interrogators who strip a man to
nakedness before subjecting him to the third degree. So, coming
down the Humber, seeing the hands about the job of squaring
up the ship dressed in the nondescript of any landsman none too
fussy over his appearance, I had to think hard about their reputation to identify them as the men they were said to be. But now
recognition was immediate. Clothing that in the stores looked
heavy and shapeless took on a lively form on them. They looked
right for the job in hand, namely driving a fishing vessel far into
the north. Used as I was to the light cotton coats and trousers of
humdrum merchant ships, the new fishing gear felt stiff, inflexible,
unworn. I changed quickly and as inconspicuously as possible.

The men off watch turned in, to read for a time and sleep, but
as decky learner, snacker, I kept no watch but was a 'dayman',

the pair of us and two of the hands being at the service of the mate for whatever work he wanted done during the three or four days of the passage.

The system of watchkeeping at sea has been designed to split up the twenty-four hours of the day so that the parts of the ship on which her navigation depends are always manned—her bridge, look-outs (including those which are electronic) and engines. Not many years ago, when seamen were thought to have no rights beyond the duty of keeping themselves alive enough to work the ship, only sufficient men were signed to split the day in two. Each man was responsible according to the log book for twelve hours' work at least, and more if the officer of the watch deemed that the safety of the ship demanded it. In British ships the day was arranged into six four-hour parts or 'watches', given the names middle (which started at midnight), morning, forenoon, afternoon, 'dogs' and first (which brought the ship to its next midnight). The dog watch, from four in the afternoon until eight, was itself divided so that the men worked a different set of hours each day. Thus on one day a man worked the middle, forenoon, 'first dog' and first, the next he changed to morning, afternoon, 'last dog' and middle. He was said to be in 'two watches', hard enough work in itself but with the constant call for all hands to work the ship even extra inroads into his sleep were normal. There is many a small ship today which goes to sea with the men under this routine (incidentally it can be recommended as a certain cure for anyone suffering from chronic insomnia).

In those days shipowners reckoned that their men were not worth the pay they doled out unless they were in a permanent state of near fatigue (I used to take a vicious pleasure, when I was working two watches, in imagining that I was mate of a ship with a fo'c's'le full of shipowners and shareholders: what a pig of a mate I was for calling out all hands). But in time—and after a hard, long-drawn-out struggle by the men against reluctant owners, a struggle which had to be taken to the very Houses of Parliament before those owners would let go of the smallest part of their profit—ships were manned in three watches, meaning that the day was divided into three and each man was responsible for no more than eight hours of it. This meant that the dogs had to be reconstituted as one watch and a man now works, both am and pm, either the 'twelve to four' or the 'four to eight' or the 'eight to twelve', thus putting together his eight hours. The disadvantage of this new routine, heavily outweighed by the gain in sleep and leisure, is that the men are always at work during the same parts of the day, which is tedious if the voyage is long.

Trawlermen are the least pedestrian of men, and even for their short voyages of no more than six days, homeward or outward bound, they do not submit to such routine. Because they enjoy a change they have split their day into unequal parts; the middle watch starts half an hour before midnight and runs four hours, the morning adds half an hour until breakfast at eight o'clock, the forenoon runs half an hour into the afternoon, and for those off watch there is a comfortable six hours for a long sleep or a read until half past six. Then it is by no means unpleasant, after a high tea, to finish off with a fine night, steering her along with an ear to a comedian joking on the radio, or music, or even an intermittent yarn with a watchmate.

As each day goes by each watch of men moves along one watch of the clock and all watchkeepers have their turn at the rough and the smooth of ship's time. There was nothing I liked more on a passage than turning out to a fine morning watch at half past three. On to the bridge with one of my mates—the third man in the galley to fetch a pot of tea up to us—and for the first half hour almost silence, little to be said but what was connected with her navigation. The 'officer' of the watch (hard to associate the word officer with a trawler, for they are far from being the sort of ships where you find gold braid and brass buttons) mate or bosun or third hand, looks ahead at the open sea out of the port side bridge windows. Neither ship nor land, no hazard in sight and a safe course, and before very long one of us offers a quiet comment. The Old Man asleep, the bridge warm, and me nicely folded behind the wheel, or tucked against the bulkhead, or with an elbow on the window ledge.

Then I can feel like beginning to expand in brain and body. The company revives and almost unnoticed our officer turns himself half into the bridge and little by little becomes involved with what we are talking of. He by no means forgets his duty but deals with it less conscientiously, allowing it no more than a sharp precautionary glance from time to time to see that no ship has closed, no shoal is under our stem, and that what is going on in no way contravenes regulations. The man at the wheel has the feel of her and all he must do is to lift an eye once or twice a minute to the compass card reflected in a mirror overhead and make his small correction to the course. At this quiet time of the day the wit of the hands is less caustic, more reflective, and points are pursued for their own sake rather than to mark up a successful piece of mockery. I have taken part in talk of science, philosophy, religion, art, the reminiscences of all present, the recounting of terrible voyages with unbearable skippers, the mouth-watering narration of a gigantic run ashore, the comparative sexuality of the females of the royal family and of the well-known love-making women of the Port of Hull, the qualities of friends and enemies, the lives of the great, meaning not only of the great world but also of the Fish Dock, in fact the bridge during a fine morning watch can sometimes, if the right chain of talk is started, be a real seagoing university.

Before tedium sets in it is time to call the relieving watch and the daymen. Then in a few minutes we see them from the bridge, coming to the fo'c's'le door one by one as they turn out of their berths, giving a quick look at the weather, scratching the stomach to let a little air round the parts of the body still hot from the bed, taking the morning piss through the scuppers, generally buttoning up the body and soul. They hurry aft for breakfast and we pass a more or less obscene remark about each one. In twenty minutes they come up to the bridge to relieve us but they may not look forward to the pleasures we have just enjoyed. Only the man at the wheel stays up in the snug compartment, for the working day now begins, and the other two, officer and all, must join the daymen on deck to work about the ship. But we amble aft to the mess-deck, to a full three-course breakfast, two or three cups of coffee, a yarn with the cook if it happens to be a day when the cook is acknowledging his friends; for cooks are men of terrible temperament, explosive and fulminating, and wrestling with the appalling problems of their little furnaces of galleys they are as liable to snarl as to hand you a hot and tasty bun. Then, in our own good time, we drift forward, and passing along the deck we might say to the man busy at his job, 'That's not the way to do that.' He will reply with an obscenity while we put a friendly arm around one another and step into the fo'c's'le for ten hours' rest. I know nothing so luxurious as to stretch the body out flat, not yet fatigued, or with fatigue behind you, to be able to afford the time to read a chapter or two without the denial to yourself of that amount of time to sleep, to kick out the legs, to feel the jump of a muscle as it slips back into place when the strain on it has eased off, to arch the back and settle the shoulders, to yawn, to switch off the light at the head of the bed and to let sleep take charge, knowing that you will not be dragged from it, half silly with the need for it, but will wake when the body has taken its fill.

CHAPTER 11

# *The Net—the Deck*

The other snacker and I went on deck to put a light covering of grease on all the *Steerwell*'s brass which was exposed to the weather, her ports and her ventilators. While we worked I looked over her and tried to understand the proper use for all her gear. In fact this was not at all difficult for the main difference between hers and that of the little old-fashioned trawlers which fished down the east side of Australia was in size and refinements. In matters of principle everything was the same and I had no doubt that the trawl itself would not be very different, save in size, to the one I knew.

The Granton trawl was no sudden invention, no revolutionary method of sweeping fish from the bottom of the sea. The problem which has always faced fishermen is simply expressed; how to stretch the net to its widest and, having spread it, how to heave it back aboard. When it came to taking fish which shoal near the surface (such as herring) the problem was solved by paying away a length of plain net up-weather of a drifting ship, and the fish, feeding along the tide, were caught in its mesh. A comparatively low-powered vessel is sufficient for the work as the net is kept spread not by drawing it through the water but by the action of the wind on the ship constantly driving it to leeward while the net itself, sheltered under the surface of the sea, streams up to the weather. To keep the net spread vertically, floats are fastened along its upper edge and lead weights, just heavy enough to stretch it downwards, along the lower one. This technique is known as drifting. A seine netter, still fishing near the surface, runs his net away in a circle, encompassing as large an area of the sea as his length of net allows him. When the time comes to take the catch aboard he heaves on a rope run through steel rings fastened the whole length of the surface edge of his net and closes it like a giant money-bag. Thus he does not have to tow his gear either. But a trawler fishes on a different principle. Instead of a suspended net streamed and left for a while, a trawler draws a bag along the floor of the ocean to catch the fish that shoal deep.

To a child I would compare the Granton trawl to a gigantic shrimping net, and all the gear of the ship has been developed to set the net in deep water at its maximum expansion and to bring it aboard weighed down with its catch.

Trawling is not to be understood as a sort of sea agriculture. A farmer raises his crop or his beasts under controlled conditions, the extent of his control representing the social and technical advances which have taken us from the hardships put up with by our hunting ancestors. But when we go after fish we have to face up again to the problems of primitive men. Although experimental work is being carried out in many parts of the world, some of it long established, commercially profitable work (like the gathering of the seaweed crop by Breton longshoremen), sea farming (meaning the controlled raising of a marine food supply) is still mainly in the future.

Trawlermen therefore are hunters; they equip themselves with the best weapons for chasing their prey, continuously moving after the migrating fish to get their living wherever they are to be found. This means that their working life is spent in some of the most terrible and dangerous places in the world, for cod and haddock, the principal quarry, enjoy the freezing environment of the Arctic and generally feed in high northern latitudes. The first essential for a trawler—conveyance and weapon combined—is to be supremely able to withstand the worst of weather.

The bottom of the sea is as hard and abrasive and as craggy as the surface of the dry land; therefore the trawl which is dragged along it must be robust and designed to ride over, as far as possible, the great variety of things which will damage it. If a shrimping net is dragged along the bottom of a pool with its mouth in a vertical plane and the belly and bag of the net flowing astern, then a part of the iron ring on which the net is braided will be in constant contact with the sand or rock. If we bend or hammer the

E

iron ring so that the bottom of its circumference is straight then we will have a miniature copy of the Granton trawl. In the trawl as it is adapted to the severe demands of the Hull ships, the flattened part of our ring is 120 feet in length and is made up of lengths of wire rope 3 inches in circumference shackled together. On to the centre sections of this rope are rove a set of giant iron beads known as bobbins. They vary in diameter from 18 inches in the middle of the rope to 10 inches at the sections halfway to its ends, the 'bunts', and are so fixed with alternating iron sleeves or washers, each about 8 inches long, that they cannot move laterally. The bobbins are partly buoyant and as the trawl is drawn across the ocean bed they ride softly over obstructions, while on the flat parts of the ocean bed they turn like wheels on the axes of their wire rope shafts. Extending away on each end of the wires carrying the bobbins, wire ropes of the same circumference, but tightly curved with discs of rubber about 6 inches in diameter and an inch thick, run out to the two extremities of the trawl. On this strong wire rope with its massive protection of bobbins and rubber the whole structure of the trawl is built up.

At the ends or 'wings' of the great foot rope two short and heavy iron bars are shackled by their reinforced or shod ends; each of them is secured to a steel shaft on which revolves the biggest bobbin in the whole gear, no less than 24 inches in diameter. The iron bars and bobbins, known as the 'Dan Lenos' (a seaman's corruption of the name of the Frenchman who developed them), are the ultimate parts of the trap's width. Stretched between the top, unshod ends of the Dan Lenos is 72 feet of heavy rope, joined to the bars by short lengths of light wire. This is the headline, forming with the foot rope the perimeter of the trawl's mouth. It is kept open by the buoyant action of very strong but light spherical floats secured with twine to the headline and forcing it upwards in the direction of the surface.

The trawl's mouth is like an arched canopy over a huge doorway making certain that fish about to be engulfed cannot escape upwards. Once between the wings of the trap and under the mesh of the canopy the fish are forced and pressed into the long tube of the bellies by the steady forward movement of the trawl and are finally trapped in the bag itself, that part of the net where the fate of the fish overtakes them and named by trawlermen the 'cods' ends'.

There is still another practical problem to be solved before fish can be taken in the net; although we are able to open the net with buoyant floats in its vertical plane, we must see that its wings are kept stretched as wide as possible or it will simply tow in a great heap from which the buoyant headline will strive to release itself. To achieve this, rudders are fastened to the two Dan Lenos which are towed on divergent courses so that the wings of the trawl are forced apart. They are called 'doors' and that is exactly their shape. But they are iron shod and contain the massive equipment which permits them to be detached from the trawl wires as the gear is hove aboard.

At the heart of all trawling operations is the winch known as the 'iron man'. To handle gear of the size and weight of the Granton trawl as modified for use in the Arctic, with all its bobbins and its iron shoeing, to say nothing of the weight of the net itself (the biggest net in use), all needs enormous power. To stream the trawl properly so that it fishes its best, to haul it and to put the fish aboard, requires a great number of varied operations. The power of the winch also has to be ready at hand for a multiplicity of jobs about the deck, some of them wanting only the exercise of brute force but some needing the extreme of delicacy. Trawlermen take as much of their work as possible to the winch and are masters of the art of leading its power into tight corners, even into the net hold or the fish room.

It is a simple steam-driven machine standing in bulk some 5½ feet high and about 9 feet wide and set on massive bearings at the after end of the foredeck under the superstructure of the bridge. The machine as it stands can perform only a very limited range of actions; its effectiveness depends on a set of leads about the deck welded to strongpoints in the ship's structure, and on the 'snatchblock', a portable fairlead which can be fixed by its hook to any handy point.

In passing I remember a few words between a hand and a mate who was at the limit of exasperation trying to clear a tangle of wires, doors, Dan Lenos and net, the result of fouling something on the sea bed.

'Where shall I put it?' said the deckie, holding up the heavy iron casting of the snatchblock and the bight of the wire which the mate wanted on the winch. In a terrible voice the mate bawled, 'Hang it round the end of yer shaft.'

What the mate meant was this: given a wire and a lead to advantage he could transmit two hundred horse power of heave to the point where he was toiling; he saw no reason for the deckie's perplexity.

Even today, when few ships carry sail, the foremast is important; and especially in a trawler for there, near the masthead, her fishing lights are housed, and from reading correctly the combination of their green, red and white colours anyone who knows his business will be able to tell with a great deal of accuracy what course the ship whose lights he has in sight is working. In an Arctic winter, when daylight is nothing more than a ten-minute glow, no more than the midday looming of the sun in the south, the knowledge gained from their lights alone of what a dozen nearby ships are up to is invaluable.

Well up towards the masthead two blocks are mounted, single sheaved and double sheaved, with the single at the top. These important members are called respectively, the jilson and the tackle. The tackle is a wire-rove purchase whose moving part with its heavy hook is stowed at the foot of the shrouds and used whenever the mate decides that the catch of fish is too great to be hove aboard with the single-rove jilson. The jilson, named no doubt after some old seafarer who first thought of working a handy hook from the masthead (or perhaps it was named after a clumsy deckie who by mistake put a turn of wire round his neck and hanged himself from that top block), is one of the most useful pieces of gear in the whole ship. Whenever a quick heave is needed—stretching out waterlogged cod ends for a quick repair to a couple of meshes, heaving a set of bobbins into place, fetching a length of new bellies up from the net hold, there is nothing like the jilson for all such little jobs. Why, with the help of the jilson I and my shipmates have even put half the ship's catch over the side when we were two hours off the Humber and the owner sent us a message that the market was glutted (the retail price of fish did not come down, by the way).

At the foot of the mast there is a massive steel structure which houses on the strongest of bearings a set of free running sheaves through which the trawl warps are led. A trawler usually fishes her gear from her side (though certain newly designed ships have reintroduced the old-fashioned stern gear still used in the Mediterranean) and one of the warps is therefore paid away from her fore part and one from aft. From these sheaves at the foot of the mast one warp is led forward from the winch drums to a powerful frame leaning about a foot over the gunwale, and the other is led aft through two more sheaves (placed so that the wire runs along the ship's side above the scuppers) to a similarly rigged frame about 35 feet forward of the stern. These frames, known as the 'galluses', triangular in shape, about 7 feet high and 5 feet at the base, are built of a single length of steel girder bent over at the apex and embedded in concrete at the foot where the two legs are taken through the deck, riveted to it at the entry, and also made fast below to the ship's ribs. They are supported as well from strong points on the superstructure by horizontal steel struts to their apexes. These are the points from which the ship does her fishing—fancifully they might be called her fishing rods —and they bear an enormous part of the weight of the trawl.

In a tow over foul ground the gear sometimes gets 'fast'; the trawler, steaming ahead, suddenly falters and there is the most ominous grinding and juddering as the weight of the advancing ship is thrown on to the winch brakes, and the galluses shake to the strain. I used to stand well clear when these little accidents happened. Though I never saw a gallus buckle or lift out of the deck, the very sight of such excessive strain on those massive pieces of steel was something which filled me with a deep respect. But they were as strong as the ship; so great was their strength in fact that it was once the cause of a terrible disaster to the trawler *Hildina*. Fast in a gale, the crew was trying to break their

73

gear clear of whatever was holding it. Without parting anything or bringing anything down they threw such a weight from the winch on to the galluses and warps that she was hove under a sea that came in at the moment of that tremendous heave, and as I remember she went with nearly all hands.

One thing more must be mentioned, a most important part of the ship's fishing equipment and the aftermost in her. It must be clear that if the trawl warps run away into the sea to the doors straight from the galluses, then the heave on those doors from the moving ship will not be constant, for as she alters course to follow her soundings over the ground she will throw variable strains on her warps. The all-important angle of constant divergence of the doors will not be maintained, and the spread of the trawl itself will be affected. Moreover, the warps have to be kept absolutely clear of the ship's rudder and screw, for not only is there the danger of the warps' being parted should they foul a blade of the screw, but even worse, and of great danger to the ship herself, is the risk of turning a bight of warp hard round the main shaft or into the mounting of the rudder. The ship is then no longer 'under command' and is at the mercy, more or less, of the weather conditions prevailing. The best that can happen to her is that she is taken in tow to clear herself in the nearest port; the worst, another of the terribly frequent disasters in the industry.

By means of the messenger, a long handy wire spliced into a hook, and a sheave welded right aft on to the gunwale they heave the two warps together and secure them in a massive block hung by a chain close over the side. From this apex the warps are held clear of the screw, which ensures they tow evenly.

The manoeuvre of putting the warps in the block requires a beautiful set of high-speed team actions. To see it done in a seaway when the ship's transom is lifting and falling 15-20 feet, when severe strain is jerked on to the messenger as the trawler rides to the seas, when the mate and the hand at the winch are managing the warps on the flexible cushion of steam in the winch cylinders, achieving the most delicate and alert co-operation between themselves and the bosun as he, working aft, calls out for a fraction of heave or slack so that he can fit the block in place, to see all this is to understand how expertly men can work their bodies in with the gear they use. They move as easily as athletes, where a mistake would cause the sudden amputation of fingers or hands, or even violent death; but the job is done calmly, with a complete control of the gear used. I have seen the warps blocked, and taken my part in doing it, thousands of times, often in brutal weather, but I have never had to witness an accident, though I knew of the terrible result of one or two.

That is nearly the tally of the running gear used by trawlermen. The rest is the deck equipment which can be found in any sort of ship, boats, anchors, capstan, fenders, gaffs, rope, wire and so on. But all this is incidental to the main job, namely fishing with the Granton trawl. It is this which lifts trawlermen out of the ruck of common seafarers. Their connection with the sea is so deep, so completely a part of their lives, that the business of driving a ship on a passage through the routine hazards of weather and pilotage takes up the minimum of their attention. Trawler skippers and mates are no wonderful navigators yet they maintain, in some of the worst conditions of the sea, precise timetables, and calmly estimate, when they set off home from such desolations as Novaya Zembla, Cape Farewell or Bear Island, their hour of arrival on the tide they need to get them into the Fish Docks. Some of them are handy enough with a sextant and a clock, others would be hard put even to lower the sun to the horizon, but they can all manage the transference of radio bearings and they are all masters of the knowledge of the tides and their sets (ie currents). What occupies nearly all the energy of officers and men at sea aboard an ordinary ship, meaning (over and above chipping and painting) steering her from port to port, to this a trawlerman gives the least of his thought. Of all men it is he who can best be said to 'work' the sea.

# CHAPTER 12

# The First Day's Work

The morning watch at the end of the first night called all hands to breakfast.

'The bastard wants a field day,' said Punch, meaning the skipper, as he shook the sleepers in the fo'c's'le. When we were sitting aft over our food in the mess room I asked what a field day was.

'It means we all do a little bit of work for nothing.' The speaker was a man named Colville. Everything he had to say he uttered as though at the final syllable of a curse.

'I never knew a skipper who could do without his field day.'

The mate said in a reasonable voice, 'Don't be like that, Colville. You know the game.'

'So I do know the game, Ernie. I know we're going to the White Sea. I know we'll be twenty-eight hours through the fiords. Why can't we fix his trap in watches inside under the lee? I'll tell you what. The bastards just like to look at us swilling about on a nice chilly deck. It makes 'em feel warm.'

'You've got a following breeze. You'll be nice and comfortable out there today. Get it fixed now and think of the sleep you'll have in the fiords.'

'Following bastards. Anyway I can't ever sleep in the fiords. I get nightmares thinking of the sport at the other end of 'em.'

Ernie put down his cup.

'Are you feeling strong then, lads?'

We followed him out on to the deck, Colville and all hands save the man at the wheel. In the engine-room they put steam on the winch and we began to heave up net from the hold under the whaleback.

To give an idea of it I compared the trawl to a shrimping net, but its mesh has a far more subtle arrangement. Its dimension decreases from four inches in the mouth and wings of the trawl, through an average three inches in the bellies to two and a half inches of double braiding at the cod ends. These dimensions have been internationally agreed and a ship discovered using smaller mesh by a Fishery Protection Officer will be very heavily fined. Skippers seldom take this risk, and in any case it would only have occurred to those less expert men who used to fish their trip on the codling banks, say at Bear Island.

'Sweeping up the future, the bastard,' said Ben, furiously gutting tiddlers alongside me during a trip we made with one of these 'rammel merchants'. Ben did not usually worry about the future but we had been eight days on this fry and his fingers were sore.

'Three of these little bastards wouldn't make a decent sprag,' and without sea boots for ten days we pushed the unsaleable small fish through the scuppers into the sea, where they died by the hundred thousand for want of the power to submerge their air-filled bodies. Food for the molly-hawks and good for our leg muscles.

The net has a shape and it must 'flow' with every mesh fully bearing its own small share of the total drag. From Dan Leno to Dan Leno the mouth of the trawl takes naturally the shape of a deep curve owing to the resistance of the water against the drag. The net is therefore tailored to this curve so that there is no distortion of the mesh. Moreover from 72 feet in the headline it tapers to about 6 feet in the last mesh of the cod ends. The taper is achieved in the same way that a woman knits a sleeve: she 'decreases' or 'increases' according to whether she works from shoulder to cuff or from cuff to shoulder and a trawlerman 'creases' as he braids from cod ends to trawl mouth and 'bates' when he goes the other way.

The number of meshes in the trawl has been worked out from experience and it remains standard. This is important when it comes to repairing damaged gear for a knowledge of the exact dimensions by mesh of the trawl enables the mate or bosun to organise the menders so that the job is finished with the net still in its right shape and its number of meshes unchanged.

Now the trawl is made up in sections, 'top wing', 'lower wing', 'bellies' and so on, and in Hull it is sent from the net lofts aboard most ships unassembled. Skippers have small differences of opinion about putting their gear together; one will want a little slack in the lacing together of a pair of bellies where another will not have them laced until their edges have been brought to each other as taut as a bar on the winch; yet another will want parts of his gear double-braided, where the strain of the net is heavy; and when it comes to cod ends I never knew two skippers who had them put together in the same way.

The job of my mate and I was to wait on the men with whatever small gear they wanted, but in particular we looked after the mate and bosun. We were the minders of a basket filled with big balls of twine, needles and odds and ends of light tools. We had to keep the needles loaded with twine for the men at work on the fixing of the trawl. They worked fast with a practised dexterity, reminding me immediately of my old Yorky shipmate in Australia. His movements of the needle through the mesh of the net were enough to show me now that he had told no lie as to where he had learned his trade. The work I was looking at had the same stamp of class about it as his.

I believe that the netting needle is one of the oldest tools that men possess. There is certainly a record of nets and fishing in the Bible; we know that the Romans used nets—they say that a swordsman was no match in the arena for a man armed with net and trident—and no doubt longshoremen fishing the Nile delta were using nets hundreds of years before that.

Except that our needles were longer, to allow for the heavy twine we used, the work we did and our tools were no doubt not much different from those of the first fisherman who ever put a needle into a net. But this morning we were not braiding net, we were joining it together. One man laced up bellies by the two selvages of the manufactured net. He put his needle five meshes deep into the selvages of the nets and drew them together with a hitch which he repeated every 4 inches right the length of his work. He worked at his 'lace-stitch' with double twine which meant that his needles had to be loaded for him with the twine already doubled. In consequence he used up his twine at twice the speed of the other hands and his voice was raised every two or three minutes in a shout for a 'needle o' double'.

The mate and two others were braiding the laced-up bellies on to the 'top part', that is the wings of the net, and the 'square', the part of the net which forms the overhanging mouth of the trawl. They braided their joining mesh around the cylindrical part of the net hitching the bellies and the top part together. They worked first along the lower side of the bellies joining them to that mesh, doubled for strength, which ran the length of the foot rope, and then they worked back along the upper side. Once they were set going the mate left them, had a look at how Punch was doing running down the lace-stitch of the bellies, and then went off to fix his cod-ends. He took with him the winch-man who was unemployed now that all the net we needed was hove up from the net loft, and called me after him to keep them supplied with needles of twine.

CHAPTER 13

# *Money*

The cod-ends are the bank; they are that part of the trawl where the fish is deposited, where the money is. They are the ultimate part of the ship and her gear; in fact they tow so far astern that you could well say a trawler is the biggest deep-water ship afloat —what other ship has a draught of 100 fathoms and an overall length of more than half a mile? Only the cable layers, which when they are working, lurching about on the end of their telephone wire, are always fast to dry land.

Since all fish that are caught flow into this small bag, no more than 10 feet long and about 6 feet wide when it is stretched out flat on the deck, and the bag becomes stuffed with the fish jostling in, it will ride over the sea bed like the rest of the net. It is dragged down with the weight of fish and scrapes along, continuously chafing its underside. Therefore it has to be protected. The mate, then, set to work.

He took two lengths of net 'bating' from a hundred meshes down to sixty. The mesh itself of this cod-end stuff is the smallest in the whole trawl, no more than $2\frac{1}{4}$ inches. He laid these two lengths of net together, stretched them taught on the winch, and with four meshes in the stitch laced their selvages up with double twine. He and the winchman worked along both sides and then laid the joined net flat on the deck. Around the aft or sixty-mesh end of this sleeve the mate now braided a single row of large meshes of double nylon twine. This was the 'cod line' mesh and the key of the safe deposit of fish. Through them he rove a light nylon rope whose heart had been removed to make it soft and flexible. We shall see when it comes to hauling the gear and heaving the fish aboard how very nicely the mate used this key.

He then secured around the bag the heavy rope which comes into use when the net is swollen with fish. By heaving on this rope a manageable weight of the haul is throttled from the net and into the bag's extreme end, the remaining cod lying afloat and awaiting their turn for a passage home.

In bad weather when the skipper is anxious to get his gear aboard and every minute counts in a race against worsening conditions, when the ship is lying vulnerable across the weather and the sea is piling in freely over the rail, when all hands are fighting to get aboard the fleets of net which are streaming upwind of us, and when they curse at the sight of an unwanted good haul lying awash in the rollers over the side, in such weather I have heard the skipper shout down to the mate, 'Take it in one!'

Once, in bad weather, we were trying to heave a full bag of fish, near 4 tons in weight, up over the side and inboard. A terrible strain was put on our gear and everyone sent a glance aloft into the foremost rigging where the double-sheaved block was groaning with the unfair load. No warning was necessary for us all to stand clear of the spot where each reckoned it would hurtle down if it parted its shackle. The winchman held the weight on the steam and the man on the tackle wire over on the lee side winch barrels took the slack off them as the bag came up. The ship rolled her weather rail down to the bag.

The art of bringing it aboard is to wait until the ship rolls to the bag and then heave until it falls inboard into the stops, a pair of hemp-covered wires which are rigged away aft from a point 6 feet high in the shrouds to a shackle on the gunwale in her waist. Their work is to prevent the incoming bag swinging freely, out of control, across the deck. If the winchman knows his job he will judge the swing of the ship, the speed of the winch, the time taken for the steam to respond to the control valve, and the weight of the bag; by instinct and from his experience he will resolve all these factors and ship that bag with the least possible strain, gently dropping it inboard.

On that bad day the winchman made no mistake. He caught the weather roll of the ship with perfect timing and hove the bag to the rail. His mate at the drums took the slack of the tackle off the winch and threw the coils down clear of his feet so that he could not be caught in a loop if the wire ran away out of control. In that dangerous weather those two men worked beautifully: every action was right. But the sea was too much for us. She lurched suddenly down to leeward and the bag swinging full at the end of its arc fetched up too heavily against the rope stops. The mate yelled out, 'Lower!' but already the mesh of the cod-ends was splitting. A roll back to the weather threw the bag into the gunwale where it broke open like a melon, and the pulp, the skipper's fish, slithered and tumbled back into the sea. A few baskets of fish remained in the bottom of the cod-ends and the winchman lowered to the deck.

'Serve him right for fishing in this bloody weather,' said the mate, thus exonerating the men at the winch from an accident which was none of their fault. But above the din of the weather we heard the bridge window slam down. ('Like a bloody third-class carriage window,' said Ben to me once on another occasion.)

'Who's on the winch?' shouted the skipper to the mate.

'Joe and Dash.'

'Yer pair of bastards,' the old man yelled, 'Ye've lost me sixty baskets of fish!'

'Pull yer bleedin' head in!' the man alongside me shouted from under the concealing cover of his sou'wester. The bridge window shut with a bang and we set about lashing and stowing our gear ready to dodge into the gale.

In two tubs on the boat deck over the galley, stowed in salt water and a solution of preserving salts, were about a dozen cow hides.

'Go and fetch me a couple of good hides,' said the mate. I went aft and dragged two of the saturated sheets of leather back along the deck, down the side of the ship where no one was working. He stretched them out and gave his knife a rub on the steel stowed in the needle basket.

'Butcher 'em,' he said. He divided them athwartships across the animal's back. I helped him by pulling the leather away from the cut as his sharpened knife sliced through it. Across the straight-cut edges of the four pieces of hide he made five holes just big enough to take a rope yarn. Then with slack yarns we lashed the hides to the bottom side of the cod-ends, arranging them so that the trailing edge of one overlapped the fast edge of the one aft of it. Our cod-ends were now ready; we had protected them as far as we could with strips of old mesh and cow hides against what was coming to them, the terrific wear and tear of the drag over the sea bottom. The mate set the hand and me to braiding them on to the small mesh of the bellies, completing the trawl.

While we others fixed the trawl the bosun and two men were aft setting up a small derrick to help the hands working there to heave their door and bobbin wires about. They rigged it so that the peak of the derrick was directly above the gallus, swung out and guyed just where the bosun wanted it. He and his team then came forward to reeve new wires through the jilson and tackle blocks.

We at the trawl worked comfortably under the lee of the bridge for the weather was following us. Before the wind she took no water over her rail and only now and again did a flood spurt inboard, splashing the deck as she rolled her scuppers under a fair-sized sea.

# CHAPTER 14

# Ten Days' Work—Shooting—
# the Watch

That was the time of the year when in the White Sea it was dark, full night for about twenty-two out of the twenty-four hours, when the sun was south of the equator and our rim of the world was getting nothing of it save a gleam, brightening and darkening at midday. Not that the sun mattered much to us, for six hours after we cleared Honningsvag and dropped our pilots there at the northern end of the fiords the skipper called us out. I did not know, that first trip, what was in front of me, and I remember now that I was not only nervous but interested, on edge, when the order came at last. But on trips after that I used to dread turning in for my last watch below.

When we did not have the watch and were not fixing gear we used to try to get as much sleep as we could on the run off, trying to store it up. But 'you can't put sleep in a bottle'; you cannot take a dram of sleep as you can of rum to liven you up. I have read that at a certain level of fatigue the bloodstream becomes fouled, poisoned, and the only thing which can restore it is plentiful sleep. This stage is reached by trawlermen after about four or five days' work; but to fill the fish room they must toil for five to seven days more. They then begin to approach the point of exhaustion; they do their work in brain shadows like men half sick; but their only sickness is a terrible need for sleep. They do a dangerous and skilful job and their main tool is their own body which tires out each trip from the quantity of work. They are safe from injuries, which the fast-running gear always threatens them with, only because of their experience, for they know their own and each other's work off by heart; though even that familiarity carries with itself its own danger when they

*Page 85*   Shooting the net once again

Page 86
(*above*) Sorting the fish in the fish pounds

(*right*) The fish are in the pounds and gutting now begins

are being overtaken by fatigue. I never knew a trawlerman who could be compared with that sort of fool in whom 'familiarity breeds contempt', but worn-out men are prone to blunder, to fumble—and a fumble has too often meant a severed limb, a stranded ship, loss of life.

On that last watch below before the fishing started I used to turn in hating the thought of the unavoidable cry of the watch coming into the fo'c's'le: 'All hands—down trawl.' Ben used to go through a pantomime of saying farewell to his berth which he combined with a cursing of whatever owner whose ship he was afloat in.

We used to go to sea in a large modern trawler with twenty or twenty-one men, which left only twelve on deck for the fishing, and only nine at any one time once the six-hour watch below had been set and the three sleepers were turned in. When the fleets have been fishing together I have towed a few yards off Icelanders and Germans and Russians. We were so near one another that we must have been taking fish from the same shoal and in the same quantities, yet within minutes of their hauling there has been no sign of a man on their foredecks; their fish has been gutted, cleaned and put below. But aboard us, once turned out from his watch below, a man prepared himself for eighteen hours of work; it was rare, between hauls, that our few men could clear the decks.

I have heard a wag shout from our deck, 'Look at the lazy bastards. They're all turned in forward.' And it was true that it used to enrage us, those foreign trawlermen—to see the evidence close alongside us of sleeping men. But the fact is that those ship's companies were up to twice our number. To give us a good watch below; to do away once and for all with the need to drive fishermen, from skippers, who worked hours even more dangerously exhausting than the hands, down to galley-lads; to stop burning up life and skill at that pressure all that was needed was the addition of another learner and four hands at an average cost to the trip of about £300. But the owners told us that economies had to be made.

When I got out on deck the floodlights were alight, deck and gear brilliantly lit up: on the mast there were multiple lights under big reflectors known as clusters; lights at the rear of the winch housed in steel basketwork were let into the foreside of the skipper's accommodation; there were six big single floods shining down on the deck from points around the forward bridge structure; and leading aft were more basketed lights set in both sides of the engine-room casing. Right aft, fixed to a 4 feet long steel peg and looking over the gunwale was the 'warp light', the light which showed how the trawl warps were leading away into the water; this light which was under frequent observation from the wing of the bridge, for it told us if our gear was spread properly. Overhead I saw for the first time in a Hull ship the gleam of our red, green and white tricolour and our all-round white. I came on deck as we were turning to bring our beam to the weather. The light of a single fisherman away in the dark swung across our horizon and disappeared forward of our whale-back.

From the loom of the bridge, just visible above our blazing floods, I heard the sharp ring of the engine-room telegraph answering the skipper's order and then the engine vibration stopped. The way came off her and we lay rolling to the weather, the breeze coming chilly across the deck.

All hands were letting go the lashings which held the trawl to the gunwale and casting off the light chains which secured the bobbin wires. The winchman opened his steam valve and the steam cracked noisily through the pipes, pushing cold, condensed water in front of it, and blowing it out of the opened cocks on the cylinder ends. Then when white steam began to pour through the cocks he shut them and the winch jerked through a revolution in freewheel, picked up to the heat and power of the steam and ran fast and smooth.

We put our gear in the water, in quick snatches with the jilson heaving over the side bobbins, wings, bellies, cod-ends, the brand new net stretching out crisp, not yet waterlogged, just in the range of our floods. I heard the telegraph in the bridge and then the engines took up their beat, but at slow speed. We began to move ahead and the mate and one hand manned the big hand-wheels of the warp brakes. The flanges of the drums revolved inside rims of steel lined with a fibrous composition, powerful brakes controlled by the tightening or slacking of massive screws. They allowed the warp to run gently off the drums, using their brakes to keep them slack. The floods shining down on the deck put the bridge windows effectively in darkness, but I could make out a glow or two of the skipper's cigarette as he stood by the wheel keeping her across the weather. As we got under way she dropped a little spray inboard and we lowered our heads to find the lee of our sou'westers, hearing the spray rattle on our oilcloth-covered domes.

We shackled the doors to the warps and at the skipper's call —'Lo-wer!'—they crashed down the reinforced side of the ship and disappeared from the range of our floods away into the sea. Off the drum ran two marks of yarn, spiked into the lay of the warp. They screwed down their brakes and held the marks beside the foot of the mast.

The telegraph rang back into the bridge and the ship began to pick up way, the skipper keeping her to the weather so that she had it just over her bow where its action pressed her away from her gear, preventing her screw fouling the running warps. We picked up our full speed for running them off and white water began to come in over her bow. We were sheltering under the lee of the whaleback, huddled into the fo'c's'le entrance; the two men aft, I made a guess, were in the galley keeping warm. Only the mate and the hand on the weather brake of the winch were exposed. As the spray crossed the deck they turned their heads down and to leeward and hunched their shoulders to prevent the water getting inside their frocks. It streamed off them and their frocks, one black and one light blue, shone with the wet under the floods.

Then the mate shouted at us under the whaleback, 'Bring the messenger forward.' The third hand said, 'Go and get the damn thing, snacker,' and I went aft to take from the bosun the sheaved hook which he passed to me outside the after warp and outboard of the gallus. I carried it forward clear of everything and scuttled back under the lee. The bridge window banged down again and the shout came: 'Pay aw-ay . . . twenty lengths!'

Slowly for a few fathoms, and then at speed as they felt the way of the ship pulling through their brakes, the two men at the winch let the warps run off the drums. The man on the weather side followed the mate, timing each of his marks as it hurried across the deck to the sheaved bollards at the foot of the mast, so that he was always just behind. They held the fast-running warps under the pressure of the brake rims so that below, on the sea bed, the great trawl doors surged forward upright and at their proper angle of spread. The mate cried out the number of his mark as it came off the spinning drum and at every fourth mark there was not one but a pair of yarns laid into the wire to show the departure of 100 fathoms. The sheaves in the bollards made a soft whirring noise as they turned, spinning freely in their oiled bearings, carrying the warps out to the mast foot and from there across the deck to the galluses forward and aft; the warps crackled and hissed as the lay of the strands cut through the surface of the sea down to the gear. They sped off and the bulk of the winch drums diminished under our eyes as the wire coiled round the core of the drums was taken away by the trawls. The speed of the drums continuously increased as the circumference of the coils got smaller. As the eighteenth mark went out the ring to the engine-room for towing speed was answered in the bridge and the way came steadily off the ship. Punch stepped out of the fo'c's'le doorway and picked up the messenger hook. The mate and his hand braked hard on the warps, making the rims screech on the drum flanges.

Punch leaned over the gunwale, his chest against the rail. He held a bight of the messenger wire in his hand and tossed the hook 3 feet up and out where it lodged over the fore warp leading off into the darkness. Then he stepped back, holding tight to the wire. The hand at the winch ran a few paces aft and picked up the other end by its tail of rope; the mate moved to the weather side of the winch, hand on the steam valve; aft, the bosun and his hand held the bight of the messenger ready to haul in the slack through the sheave on the rail when Punch let go. He looked round to see that all were ready and then dropped his arm. His long call sounded out—'Aw-ay!'—the winch roared at full speed and the spinning barrels picked up the weight of the two warps. They completed the beautiful movement of putting them into the towing block. The mate walked aft and glanced over the side to check the spread of the gear. 'All right!' he shouted, up to the bridge, and in answer we heard the ring of the telegraph, the reply from the engine-room to the skipper's signal that we were towing.

CHAPTER 15

# The Rig—the Watch—the Cook

Stowed under the whaleback in a locker was a stack of planks of heavy timber. In their damp sides numbers were burnt which were the key to the puzzle we now set about solving. From the deck short stanchions rose, so constructed that the planks could be slotted three deep in them. Our job was to lug out the half-saturated timber and to line it up in pairs of stanchions, thus dividing the foredeck on the side of the ship from which we were towing into six boxed-in compartments. These were known as the fish pounds.

'You'll be whiling away a bit of time here, snacker,' a hand called Mac said to me. He was the fish room man, a job much sought by trawlermen, for on his expert knowledge of the stowage of fish depended the ship's success on the Hull market. The mate, who was finally responsible for the condition of the catch, used to reward a good fish room man on settling morning with a backhander of a five pound note. Furthermore during the manoeuvre of getting the fish on deck and dealing with the cod-ends he worked with the hauling parts of the jilson, the tackle, and the little slip hook whip on the derrick peak which we called the 'yo-yo'. His place was on the barrels on the lee side of the winch and when he was not holding turns on them for a heave he could shelter from the worst of the weather behind the structure of the skipper's cabin. He was also called the lee side deckie and among men who knew only too well what the weather side of a trawler was like it was counted a comfortable job.

Ben, that schooner-rigged deckie, used to reckon to borrow one of my frocks and sou'westers in a ship we were afloat in. We had been going steady in her for four or five trips and the mate had me as fish room man.

'What are ye worrying about,' he said once as he clambered

into my spare gear, 'Ye don't need gear on your side of the platform.' He used to take a delight in comparing the deck of a trawler with the most unlikely things; that trip she was a concert platform, we were the piccolo players, the winch was the percussion, the operator was the first fiddle and the skipper was the conductor; 'Sea major', he called to the mate as the doors crashed down the ship's side and into the water when we shot. He loved a pun and went to some trouble to explain his to us. Other trips we were a railway station with the trains, meaning the gear, coming in and out and the passengers, meaning the cod, alighting. Once she was a cattle ranch out west and we, the cowhands, were 'coralling a few cod'; on that trip, I remember, we became such cowhands and men of the West that even the cook was driven mad; instead of shouting 'break-*fast*', or 'dinner-*O!*' or 'tea-*O!*' from his galley door at mealtimes he used to bellow '*chuck!*'.

The fish room man, Mac, and his deputy now opened up the two hatches aft of the mast and signed to me to follow. I climbed after them down a vertical steel-runged ladder into the quiet and chilly atmosphere of what was known as the mortuary. It was a room about 35 feet long and stretched the beam of the ship, narrowing at the forward end to the shape of the *Steerwell*'s hull. Amidships, about 6 feet above the floors, was a platform on which we stood, with about 7 feet of room overhead. On either side of this passage was a series of stanchions built from floors to deckhead, solid members of squared steel with slots on each of their four sides, The stanchions were part of the supporting structure of the deck but they also had another purpose, for in their slots boards of duralumin could be dropped building up rectangular compartments for depositing our catch; thus it was prevented from moving about in bad weather. We were our own stevedores and no ship has its cargo more carefully stowed. There were eighteen of these compartments, varying in width from the big ones aft which spanned the ship's widest part and which were all known as the after fish room, to the very small ones in the forward fish rooms which were cramped into the curve of the hull at the extreme fore end.

All the thwartship boards had been slotted into place in the after room and the fore boards rigged to a height one board above the stage we stood on. Forward, through the hatch on the fore side of the mast now battened down, had been loaded about twenty-five tons of cracked ice which had filled up eight of the pounds and the first 8–10 feet of the stage. It lay blue-white and clean, marred only in one pound by the blood from the cook's joints of meat which had been stowed there. But it did not please Mac.

'The blasted stuff's gone hard.'

We stripped off our mittens and top gear.

'The trouble with this cow is you can't get the temperature low enough down here.'

It was true the ice had a too blue look about it where water had melted, frozen again and bound it tight. It had happened because the *Steerwell* was a coalburner and to give her enough fuel for a twenty-one-day voyage the four big pounds at the after end of her fish room had been filled with coal. This was the coal first consumed on the voyage and the door through to the stoke-hold had to be left open until it was all burnt. As the firemen cleaned and trimmed and stoked up the three furnaces a little heat would seep forward and touch our ice and congeal it. It was always hard to break down the ice in a coal-burning trawler.

The fish room coal had to be taken laboriously aft into the stokehold through a tunnel 4½ feet high, basketful by basketful. If this coal was not fully burnt up by the time fishing commenced it caused trouble. After the coal was cleared into the stokehold and the watertight tunnel door locked, then the whole of the after fish room had to be washed down with the greatest care and then rigged to receive fish; the floor boards had to be lifted and the pump filters cleared of the coal dust and chips which might clog them. If the job was not done by the time the ship was on the ground then the crew, trying to battle with the cleaning and stowage of the incoming cod, would also have to pass weary hours in the meticulous preparation of those after pounds. But luckily for us our fish room coal had been burnt in good time and we had been able to do the main part of this work as we came through the fiords. All that remained now was to break up and pass aft enough ice to put a 6-inch bed on the floors of the big pounds for the cleaned fish to lie on.

'If we were an oil burner all this bloody toil would've been done by this,' Mac observed. 'You'd better get hold of that axe, snacker, and break a bit down.' There were three long-shafted axes below and a number of shovels. The deputy and I took our weapons and attacked that hard ice. It was heavy work and chopping out the congealed stuff was made harder by the rolling of the ship. We worked down enough ice, and passed it aft to Mac, to cover four floors; then we cut a pile which we left on the stage ready for sprinkling with the shovel among the stowed fish. We were sweating when we regained the deck and dropped the hatch covers into place.

On deck they had rigged the 'washing machine', a metal tank about the size of a small dinghy and mounted on rollers so that it could be moved back and fore above the fish room hatches on a pair of steel rails. Both its ends could be opened by removing a slotted shutter, and from the now opened after end they were adjusting on to the forward lip of one of the hatches a ladder-like frame containing a set of free-running rollers. When the rollers were in position they made the washer fast with wire guys and turnbuckles. Then they screwed into it a rubber pipe from the deck water system. From the gutting pounds we threw fish into the washer which swilled about in there from the rolling of the ship and cleaned itself, in the running water, of the blood left in it from gutting; as we threw gutted fish into it so a few of them were continuously spilled down the rollers into the fish room.

When all this work had been done and we were ready for the cod and haddock to come aboard, Ernie the mate weighed up the deck with a glance all round and then called out: 'All right, lads, let's get aft.'


We drew pint pot mugs of tea from the kettle which the cook had put out in the mess room, pulled up the skirts of our frocks and sat down for a cigarette, sea-booted legs expanded comfortably. We had been towing for about an hour and a half. Ernie was still standing; he pulled up the front of his frock and delved into the cross pocket of his fearnoughts for pouch and matches.

'What about the watches then?' he said.

Now the custom when the ship is fishing is for the mate and bosun to carry one decky learner and one spare hand in their watches. The other four men are divided between the third and the fourth hands. Only Punch and I were fresh aboard and it so happened that we were replacements for men from the mate's watch. Him we now joined, and since he had taken the last watch of the run-off, he, and with him Punch and I, were due for the first watch below of the fishing.

Where we had divided ourselves into three watches for the run-off, and would be so divided again when the time came for the run home, we were now in four and were to work what was known as 'eighteen and six'. Here was the essential difference between fishing and making a passage. Until we reached the fishing grounds we were free (unless the mate wanted all hands to fix gear) when off watch to yarn, to read a book, to dawdle over our meals and to sleep; we could take as much of that last valuable commodity as a man reasonably wanted. But once on the grounds the time not spent in the berth on your watch below belonged to the gear and to the fish.


The majority of trawlers worked eighteen and six, though there were a few skippers who liked to split the day into 'fifteen and five'. Not much mathematical ability is needed to see that in both systems the proportion of sleep to work is the same, namely one hour to three. Nevertheless small advantages were to be had, I used to think, from fifteen and five. In the first place, since the cycle of fifteen hours' work and five hours' sleep amounts only to twenty hours while the clock gives us twenty-four, it meant that your watch below advanced by four hours every day and that you worked and slept at a varying time. In that strange polar part of the world where broad daylight extends for nearly three months of the year and black night, relieved only by a little mid-day gloaming, takes three more winter months to pass, and where the change of declination of the sun is excessive and disturbing during the equinoctial months, up there, you may think, with day-light keeping such exaggerated hours, it is of no great value to a man to make a daily change in his hours of work and sleep. But in fact a change does make a very real difference to him. The mate, for example, traditionally turns in after tea at 7pm, and out again at midnight so that he will be as fresh as possible to relieve the skipper on the bridge, and carry on fishing, shooting, hauling, and dealing with whatever else has to be dealt with while the old man goes below. Sleep, however, does not suit the adult human body during these hours. I remember nearly exhausted trawler-men wasting precious minutes on an extra cup, a cigarette, a short yarn, before they went forward to sleep away uneasily these unsuitable hours. Moreover, their short sleep done with, they have to turn out when the body's need for it is greatest. To work hard in the hours following midnight, to know then that of the whole crew you are the furthest away from rest, is misery. And ten days of it makes deeper cuts into physical reserves than even the other sleep-deprived deck men suffered.

There is another disadvantage of eighteen hours on deck and six hours below which is entirely due to the tricks trawler owners have played on their men. The watch changes at 6.30pm, 12.30 (after midnight), 6.30am and 12.30 (afternoon), while meals are ready at 6.00 (breakfast), 12.00 (dinner) and 6.00 (tea), all of them equally substantial and essential to maintain strength. Now the rule in trawlers is that the deck and the bridge must together always be manned by at least three men, so when the cook calls the men aft, of the nine men on deck only six may leave it; the unfortunates left out in the weather are the men of the next watch below. Their meal is to come a half hour later *and will be eaten during the time they are said to be below*.

Worse still, already suffering petty injustice, they have to inflict more petty injustice on their mates. For one of them steps into the fo'c's'le, shouts out 'Watch-O!' and then rives the three sleepers awake. They, thickheaded, sullen from the need for completed rest, drag themselves from their berths, clamber back into the few articles of gear which they bothered to take off five hours before, and walk aft to a meal they can hardly stomach. But the men know that they badly need good food if they are going to get through their allotment of work. Therefore, hungry before turning in, they cram a big meal as fast as they can into their stomachs, and when they turn out most of them take as much, in even shorter time, as the stomach will hold without rejecting it. It is no wonder that the majority of men scarcely speak during the first hours of their spell on deck, for while they are recovering from the physical shock of being wakened before their time and simultaneously trying to digest their food, it is all they can do to continue working.

Eighteen and six is a gaffer's lie; that system should be called eighteen and five or even nineteen and five, for like many trawlermen, I hold that the half-hour meal break, used simply to stoke food in the stomach and recharge with energy, is time that the gaffer owes the men. I still hope today, as I write this down, that a gaffer's own food chokes him mouthful by mouthful and that the best he gets from his meals is nothing but more inflammation on his ulcer.

I used to marvel at the good nature of trawler cooks. I never met one who was not a master of his trade and some had about their work a touch of real artistry. They cook on a coal oven and work to the absolute rigidity of a trawler timetable. They bake fresh bread every two days, beautiful crusty stuff which itself was a pleasure to eat, a different class of food from that machine-handled muck, only fit for sopping up gravy, which goes under the name of bread ashore. They cook fish better than I ever ate it anywhere. True, they have the best of fish, but how many cooks make the best use of the best food? They cook good soup and especially I remember the way that some of them used to turn out fish soup made from small halibuts. They cook good meat dishes and again I remember the appetising, healthy red colour of boiled beef with carrots, onions and dumplings. Some of them used to embellish the mess room with little delicacies, tab-nabs, they were called, little hot cakes of cheese and potato or some sort of savoury tart. And before they turned in at night they used to lay up a table of cold food to keep us going until breakfast.

They cook in the most terrible weather always seeing to it that men are never short of hot food. I am thinking now of a trawler on a run home, three days out from Hull and chasing hard for the tide at the lock gates. The skipper should have reduced speed in the weather we had, a full gale almost astern of us. The big rollers were lifting us, throwing us on and twisting the little ship about in her track. I could not get along the deck from the bridge to fetch a pot of tea for the green water that was surging inboard over her gunwale.

I went aft over the engine-room casing and down through the galley hatch. The cook had crammed himself in between the galley bulkhead and his table. He was rubbing the back of his scalded hand with butter. The stove was sizzling and smoking with food spilt on its hot top. The galley floor was awash with a wave she splashed in over the coaming; cooked potatoes and carrots swilled about there freely. He looked at me almost in tears. 'She dropped the soup off the stove,' he said. 'Me heart's too full, Steve. Will ye tell the stormy bastard to ease her in.' But we had our hot dinner that day, and even soup served in pots, although that old man still kept her going.

While we were sitting down to our food during the fishing the cooks used to station themselves alongside the door or by the serving hatch between galley and mess room. They kept the galley-lad beside them, ready at a flick of a finger—I floated with one who used to make this signal as though he were the head-waiter bringing forward one more of his men—to bring out another platter of food, or take away a dirty dish. They seemed to be solicitous for us, troubled about our welfare, and anxious, as far at any rate as food was concerned, to see that we had all the comfort possible. I never knew one who gave more attention to the skipper and mate and engineers, eating below in the cabin, than he did to us in the mess room; and woe betide the galley-lad who was not back quick to serve us after he had taken food down the companionway. For cooks, in their lonely struggle with food, and shut away in their little hot hells of galleys, develop concentrated powers of the tongue. I never heard a man curse like a crossed trawler cook. These were the men, then, whose food we used to insult three times every day, cramming it into the gut to give ourselves time before being recalled to the deck to roll and smoke a cigarette. I used to wonder how they put up with us.

Skippers who worked us fifteen and five used to lose a few hours of our toil, for only rarely did meal times coincide with the change of watch; thus we could go from the deck straight to our beds, our half hour for food being sacrificed by the gaffer instead of by us. But the very worst way that eighteen and six punished us was simply this: eighteen hours of work was too long. When fishing was heavy or the gear was being damaged by rough ground we passed the last three hours of our time on deck in a sort of torpor, as though we were in hypnosis and had been ordered to persevere with motions which were not quite familiar; sometimes we felt as though we were under a narcotic which had the effect of blurring the outline of the things we looked at, and of making the hands insensitive to the things we touched. The extra hour below in no way made up for the weight of those last three hours.

I remember a fine summer's morning in the White Sea when for six days we had had nothing but heavy hauls. We were gutting cod in the pounds, standing on fish, and with fish deep around our thighs, so high on the deck that we did not even have to stoop to pick up a cod for gutting, knowing that when we hauled the gear another ton would slither over the mass we already had. We were hours from getting even the soles of our boots on to the deck planks. Alongside me as we gutted a hand by the name of Skinner, only two hours from his watch below, was telling an endless yarn. It was about a taxi and a driver with whom he was friends, women, and drinks they had all taken together, a journey in the cab to the neighbouring town of Beverley, an incident in a public house there, in fact it was a tale rich with material. But he was too tired to make it come alive. His voice wore on, a solitary chorus to the gutting, which all on deck had long stopped listening to. But he could not cease talking. Suddenly, exasperated, the bosun cried out,

'Bloody hell. What's the bastard talking about?'

'I don't know,' said poor Skinner, coming back to life. 'I do feel dippy, bosun.'

One other thing occurs to me now when I think of watch-keeping; it is that the kind-hearted skippers were the ones who worked us fifteen and five; the men with the terrible reputations never thought to work anything but the long period, while those who were only just on top of the job, or who were always worry-ing about the quantity of the catch, could never afford to spare us the half hours we would have won from our meals by not working the full eighteen and six.

So now we sat in the mess room waiting for the first haul. Punch said, 'Might as well get what's left out of this bloody watch.'

'Aye, I'm off.' The mate agreed with him. We two walked forward; we took off our frocks, boots and smocks, loosened our trouser buttons and rolled into our bunks. The fire was roaring up the stack, the fo'c's'le was warm, our blankets were cosy.

'I could stay here for ever,' said Punch.

CHAPTER 16

# Ten Days' Work—Cod

They were blocking the warps with the messenger when Punch
and I came on deck. The wind was fresh and I was glad to feel the
dram of rum Punch handed me still warm in my throat. We made
our way aft down the port side of the ship clear of the fish and
the gear to starboard.

'They're waiting for you,' shouted Colville as we passed, 'Are
you ready for them, snacker?'

The cook had not yet gone to bed when we came into the
galley. 'Here, have one of these.'

'No, Joe, thanks,' Punch answered. 'Nothing to eat. Can't eat
when I roll out. Have you got the tea?' We poured out potfuls
and I took one of the cook's hot pies. We went through to the
mess room and sat quietly with our tea. In a few minutes the mate,
fully rigged for the deck, joined us and nodded round, friendly
but silent. Over head on the forward bulkhead was mounted the
slave driver, the mess room clock, its hands pointing to seventeen past midnight. I thought it must have been the weight of the
minute hand swinging it down to the half hour, so fast did it
move when the eyes were off it. Then Ernie said, 'Are you fit,
lads?' and exactly on time we went out to the pounds.

We stepped over the planks slotted athwartship across the after
pound and without a word the fourth hand, Mac, and a red-haired
young hand known as Ginger stood upright, rapped their knives
on the pound boards to dislodge scales and congealing gut from
the blade slot, and went forward to the warm little fo'c's'le under
the whaleback.

In the two after pounds the mate and the bosun worked, the
planks in front of them canted in the stanchion just sufficiently to
let through a fair-sized cod. Around their feet was a mess of
blood, guts and a few small fry which they examined all the time

102

Page 103 (above) The fine lines of a deep-sea trawler on passage; (below) crashing through stormy seas on her way to the far northern fishing grounds

*Page 104*  (*above*) The freezing terror of winter trawling; (*below*) one of 'the North Ships' fighting on

they worked to see that no saleable fish was lying in it. The tilt of the deck kept this broth moving slowly aft where it piled up against the after boards, moving to the roll of the ship. From time to time the bosun lifted the pound boards astern of him and let the waste slide through. In the waist of the ship, just forward of the break of the deck, was the scupper port with its plate pulled up clear in its slots so that the sea could wash in and take the muck overboard. A great population of molly-hawks wheeled about, crying and screaming, some of them swooping down and hovering just outside the scupper port, beaks open and heads thrusting as they strove to get at the food they wanted. Others, fed, lay hove to on the water, stemming the weather but occasionally flying a few yards to keep up with the *Steerwell*'s towing speed.

Forward of the mate and the bosun, Colville and the deputy and the third hand worked. In their pound was the bulk of the fish and they were standing with the cod well up to their knees. Every few minutes the bosun grunted a word and Colville, inboard of the other two, booted through the raised board a basket or two of cod. Punch and I stepped heavily through the fish and into the forward pound where we joined my mate, the other snacker, and a hand who worked there in silence. We two went right to the forward end and faced aft.

In the Australian trawlers fish are not gutted. The fact is that in that country of belligerent labour traditions an odd impasse had been reached between owners and men. The owners wanted the fish gutted but they refused to ship the extra crew which the hands reckoned necessary for the job. They therefore, on their part, declared that they would fish the ships but would in no circumstances gut the catch. By good luck more than by intelligence the owners solved their difficulty for the ships rarely made voyages exceeding ten days and it was found, on landing the catch, that in spite of the guts remaining in it, deterioration had not advanced far enough to affect its sale. For this reason I never ate fish bought from a wet fish shop in Australia and, for the same reason, I never learned to gut.

I picked up a fish now in a cotton-gloved hand and aimed my knife in the direction of its stomach. It twisted in my hand with

G

the remains of its powerful vitality; the point of the knife slipped harmlessly down the side of its belly and dropped from my grip among the ungutted fish in the pound. I completed the ham-fisted performance by letting the cod slither back among his brethren from my too tightly squeezed fingers. I turned to Punch: 'How do you do it?'

'Easy,' he said.

But before Punch guts his fish, before this neat and dexterous operation can be seen, something must be known of the fish we were after.

When I think of fish I always come back to the memory of a live cod. There are certain species which seem to sum up in their own existence all the possible properties of their general race. I am no scientist and I put this view forward only with the greatest caution, but the fact is that when the word 'animal' comes into my mind it is accompanied by the picture of a bear, a sort of medium-sized brown shaggy bear, omnivorous, able to survive well in nearly all climates, and having in his utilitarian frame some part, however small, of the abilities of all animals. And the word 'man' comes in with a picture of a hard and nutty Mediterranean sort of man, not too big, not overspecialised in any one direction, but very able in everything he does. To me birds are gulls, dis-persed all over the world, amphibious, assertive of their vitality, finding nourishment everywhere and very likely as a species to survive. And so when it comes to fish it seems to me that cod are the most typical. Take their appearance: in the first place they are a deep-hulled fish, far more satisfactory to look at than the flat-bottomed mudhoppers like plaice, skate, sole, and so on; second, their designer achieved a very nice compromise between speed, cargo capacity, and armament. They have a good broad head, well streamlined, with the mouth coming away wide on each side and protected by good fleshy lips. They have not much in the way of teeth but make up with a pair of strongly serrated gums which are well able to dispose of the food they take. Where other creatures have necks the cod has his gills, neatly fitted behind a bony plate and enclosing the membranes through which he filters his breathing water. The underside of his mouth is elastic and his jaw mechanism enables him so to articulate it that he can engulf, whole, a fish nearly one-third of his own size, and work the meal back into his belly. Coming aft from his gills are his topsides which round away and fine into his tail right astern. His belly is fared into the gills and is supported forward by a pair of heavy bone ribs so shaped that he can lay his gills back into them in the closed position as tight as a watertight door. Under those two ribs he carries his two stabilisers, a pair of light thwartship fins which keep him upright when he is on course. From there his belly curves in a nice sheer up to his tail. Fore and aft along his backbone are rigged the three fins thought by all the cod specialists I ever knew in Hull to be there for his protection.

There you have him then, a streamlined fish with a round stem and a deep draught, wide in the head but fining away to a strong but slender stern and tail. His colour is dark mottled green on his back, lightening to white on the underside of his belly and mouth. Stretching right the length of his body from jaw to tail is his boot-topping, a light but clearly defined grey line. Speckled all over his green topsides are little flecks of gold leaf, and when the light shines on him from a certain angle you can see a faint touch of red. Unluckily for all those who know a cod only when he is stretched out on a fishmonger's slab (or appears as a steak or a piece of fillet) his beautiful varied colours disappear, seeming to need his strong vitality to make them sparkle.

Unlike fish that live near the surface—such as shark, mackerel, herring and others—and unlike also those who need to be within reach of the sea-bed in great depths of water—fish so rarely seen by fishermen that it has been left to scientists to give them ugly latinate names—the cod does not seem to worry much in what depth he finds himself in his foraging. I have caught him on a shoal bank in 15–20 fathoms and I have caught him in 180, so deep that we have had only a couple of lengths of warp left on the drums while we were towing, and it has taken us all of half an hour simply to haul the gear. For all I know he could probably be taken in 500 fathoms if we had gear good enough to lift him.

He lives well most of the year, keeping plenty of flesh on his frame, but like everything else he starts to be a little bit thin during the spring. In the autumn and early winter he attends to the future of his race, and the guts of himself and his female are embellished with the growth of a set of very succulent roe, a pale oatmeal colour showing through the membrane covering the lobes of his, and a rich pink through hers. The roes are one of the valuable extras he provides and are collected by trawlermen in little sacks which are iced away in the fish room; 'bags of gold', these are called. The other, even more valuable extra—as far, at any rate, as trawlermen are concerned, since in its unrefined state its oil belongs entirely to them—is his liver, at its heaviest and oiliest in the late summer but on the rich side during the whole year, save for a month or so of the early spring when he consumes it, no doubt to keep himself alive. He then leaves for poor fishermen only a fibrous, rubbery scrap of tissue known as a 'boot-lace' and for all the oil it renders hardly worth the trouble of collecting. He roams about in search of his varied diet all over the Northern hemisphere; a few of them, marked by scientists with a little metal tag in the gill and later taken in a trawl, have been known to survive very long passages. Certainly they find it no trouble to voyage from Norway to the Newfoundland Banks by way of Iceland and Greenland, and they probably navigate the North-west Passage, north of Canada, and the North-east Passage, north of Russia, into the Pacific.

At his most rewarding he is about 3 feet long, weighs live about 10 pounds, and will have a nice oily liver of about 10 ounces. As for eating, he is to the taste of fish what steak is to the taste of meat—there is nothing better except those fish which taste rare and also cost it.


'Do it like this,' Punch said. He laid the fingers of his left hand across the top of a cod's head and sought with his thumb the soft part under the lower jaw. He picked him up and turned the head of the sprag—as a good sized cod is called—against his thigh with the belly outward. He canted the cod slightly to one side, laying bare the left gill which was lifted from its seating by the weight of the fish's body. He now had the whole housing of the gill exposed, the red filtering membrane displayed and spread out. Putting the point of his knife above the breastbone, he made his incision, sliding the knife alongside the bone until it reached that point under the cod's jaw where the two breastbones came together; there he turned the edge of his knife down to the cod's tail and with it felt for the narrow division between the bones. He found it and ran the knife down the belly to the anus. Only the tip of the knife was used for this long cut, and as he made it he transferred his thumb into the opened belly, still supporting the fish with his fingers but holding it firm by the lug of flesh and bone which he had just laid back. Holding the knife in his palm by the pressure of the third and fourth fingers he lifted out the fat liver with his thumb and the first two and dropped it in the basket which we shared in the pound. The cod's gut now hung down free. He put the blade of his knife under the gullet, at the extreme top end of the hanging gut, and into that fibrous tube made his last incision. With a rapid up and down movement of his knife hand he ripped out the gut and dropped it on the deck and then with finger and thumb removed the little knob of a heart seated in a fold or fibre behind the fish's head on its right side. He then swung the fish away with his left hand, tossed it ten or more feet into the washer, and reached for another.

He had worked slowly, showing me each of the operations, but now he returned to his work at his own speed, and Punch, a good man with a knife, was able to maintain for hours at a time a steady pace of between eight and twelve fish a minute depending on their size. He turned away from me then, decisively, as though to say: 'You've got to learn to do this quickly if you're going to be any use to us.' I learnt as fast as I could, for with no skill at the knife I was of no use to the crew. No matter how good a hand you were—and I am certainly making no special claims for myself—no matter how expert with the gear, if you could not learn to maintain the pace of gutting then there was no room for you in the industry.

To complain about the burden of going through these motions

tens of thousands of times in the course of a trip, hundreds of thousands of times in the course of a year, millions of times in the course of a life; gutting in conditions where hard, fully adult, men have been in severe pain from the agony of long-frozen fingers; gutting when the articulation of the small bones in the wrist has been impaired by the strain on them which has made the wrist swell up fat and pulpy, when the bones can be clearly heard to click if the painful joint is swivelled a foot from the ear, when the lively wriggle of a codling in the hand intensifies the pain; gutting when the wrist has been chafed raw by the sleeves of the frock and the pads of the fingers hurt from the abrasive wear on them of fish guts and skins; gutting in spite of a cut, perhaps earned from the careless handling of the rags of a wire splice, which has worked deep into the flesh as the sea water has attacked it; gutting when each movement to pick up a fish has sent pain through overtired muscles in the back; always maintaining speed; gutting in spite of the tedium of the job, when, say, after midnight the gutters face the cod and haddock knowing that tons more is still to be hove aboard before the skipper has had enough; and knowing all the time that the worst of the burden could be lifted off us simply by the employment of a few more hands: to complain about any of this, to complain even to yourself, was to be a fool. The fact that British trawlermen go to sea in ships which are badly undermanned is of no matter at all to a crew working on the grounds. Once out there the main task is to shift the fish from deck to fish room as fast as possible for there may be a chance of a cup of tea and a cigarette in the mess room before the next haul, or even the chance of a rare half-hour's straighten out in the bunk forward.

And so I started to learn how to gut, but it was eight or ten trips before I gained any facility with the knife.

CHAPTER 17

# The Trawler 'Frances'

'What did you come this way for, Steve?' Punch asked me as we
stood in the pound. By this time I had learnt the movements of
the knife sufficiently to take a few minutes at least off from thinking about it, and join in a yarn. I told him about my old shipmate
in Sydney—old Yorky.

'What did they call him, snacker?' the bosun asked.

'George Cook.'

'You remember him, Ernie.' The bosun turned to the mate.
'He paid off the Navy over there.'

'Aye,' Ernie said; he filled in the identification. 'You mean
Cook who was cousin to Lofty Long—used to go bosun in
Rasmussen's.'

Colville set us back in the present. 'Did the lying old bastard
tell you to come to Hull then, Steve?'

They were doing old Yorky an injustice for he had told me
only that I might be 'all right'.

'Old trawlermen ought to keep their mouths shut,' Punch said.
'If I hadn't listened to our old man I wouldn't have come this
way.'

'Aye, but you had two chances, Punch. You must've been
silly.'

'How did you get two chances?'

'I was in the *Frances*. I was third hand in her when she went
ashore.'

Three years before the trawler *Frances* went to Greenland for a
trip there during the early winter season. They got beyond Cape
Farewell and started fishing up the west coast. Though fish was
normally plentiful on that coast—as though to make up for the
hazards of a winter passage there and back across the North
Atlantic—the *Frances* was short of her daily average. Further-

more the weather set in so bad that they had lost haul after haul through having to dodge into the depressions sweeping past them.

A gale can often bring a welcome relief to a trawlerman. He takes not much notice of the enraged weather, save to make sure that the deck gear is well secured, and when fishing must stop uses the opportunity to turn in for a long sleep. The ship lies up to the weather like a gull and only the duty watch, three men of the twelve, need to be about; for once the fish is gutted and below, once the gear has been overhauled and repaired, the rest may turn in to sleep. In their seaworthy ships they worry, not about the strength of the gale or about the tremendous movement of the hull over the ridges and valleys of the oncoming seas, but only whether these conditions will last until they have worked out their sleep.

Unluckily for the *Frances* she was in a position at the edge of the travelling depressions where the weather was fining and freshening in such a fluky rhythm, without once settling into a plain gale, that she could not fish steadily, nor could the men get below; for the skipper was not managing to keep her out of trouble. At nearly every haul which they did make the trawl surfaced damaged—ripped in the wings, ripped in the bellies, parted in the headline. Punch told me they had needles in hand all the time. After four days' work they had no more than five hundred kit of fish aboard where they should have taken between eight and nine hundred at the least for a fair trip.

Then the weather began to freshen really badly. The skipper decided, when the trawl came up so damaged that it all had to be hove aboard for repair, to get further up the coast to the north and try to change his luck. He let his ship lie for an hour while the mate and the crew completed the worst of the mending and put what fish they had below, then called for the gear to be lashed securely and the hands to get forward off the deck.

By the time they had been under way for half an hour it had darkened and the weather had come in thick and sleety with the wind. The bosun had the watch, for the skipper, as tired as any man in the ship from the hours he had put in during those first four days, had set his course and handed over in the same way as he had done hundreds of times in the past. Unless the weather hardened they were not to call him until she had run off her distance.

At the enquiry later they asked Punch what he thought had happened. 'Don't know,' he said. 'When she struck I was thrown out of my bunk.'

'Tell us in your own words what happened then.'

'Well, all the lads made a dive for the fo'c's'le door. I was last because I just took time to drag on my frock. And then I couldn't get through the fo'c's'le alleyway, for she took a heave on the rock and lay down on her port side. When I did get to the door she was being swept.

'All hands must have been taken when she went over. I couldn't see anything for the seas coming in and the sleet, and you couldn't hear anything for the noise of the weather. The tackle hook must have chafed adrift and it was swinging about on the end of the falls.

'I stayed where I was in the alleyway and I kept well in for fear of the watertight door. It was still hooked back but hanging nearly overhead because of the way she was lying. Then a big one seemed to get under her. I thought that was the end of me. I thought she was coming off. But she went further up. You couldn't hear anything for the noise of the hull on that rock when she went over it. The hook on the fo'c's'le door went and that door came down with a bang and hung free. I reckon that's what saved me for she was taking terrible water on board by this. She would've swilled me out of the fo'c's'le. But I battened the door down from inside and when one came over her I could hear it running over that door. It was sprung a bit where the bottom should have been tight and water was getting in there now and then.

'I went back into the fo'c's'le and then I had another bit of luck. The way she came up you'd think shed've unshipped the fo'c's'le stove and put all the berths and bedding afire and smoked me out. But it was still there and also it was out because of the water coming in the stack. I reckon the cowl had gone.'

'What did you do?'

'Well, I didn't do anything—not what you might call saving the ship. The lads had gone and I thought the ship and me was going soon. I couldn't really tell what the weather was like because of the noise she was making grinding about on that rock, and all the banging on deck. By the feel of her I thought she was held just forward of midships and all the fore end of her was clear, but I couldn't tell for sure. She was being swept now and again but she must have been taking the main damage aft and midships.'

'Then what happened?'

'Well, I made myself comfortable as best I could and climbed up clear of the water that was swilling about in the fo'c's'le. It was no good thinking of what would happen if she slipped and went, and I didn't want to think about what would happen to me if she stove in the side she was chafing on, or the whaleback which was keeping me dry.

'I was sat there on the fourth hand's berth so I felt under his bedding for his bottle. It was there all right, fallen down against the fore and aft board. It wasn't broken and there was about half of it left. [This part of the story Punch said nothing about at the enquiry, but I put it in here to reconcile the bar-room tale with the narrative in the courtroom—one of the chances which saved that man's life.] They called the fourth hand Joe Fisher and I was glad Joe'd taken it by the dram. Anyway I sat there and supped it all up and then—well, I bobbed off.

'I got woken up by a terrible hammering noise but all the other clatter had calmed down. Then I remembered where I was and made a dive for the fo'c's'le door—that was where it was coming from. Somebody called out and I shouted back. Then I couldn't get the clamps off the fo'c's'le door, but whoever it was had a hammer on deck and they brayed them free. They heaved the door up and I jumped out and went straight down the deck into what was left of the port-side gallus. It was near under water and I got my fearnoughts wet under my frock. I don't know why I bothered with that frock—would've been no good to me if I'd had to swim—automatic, I suppose, and lucky I did the way things turned out.

114

'It had fined away and there was just the roll coming inboard up the deck. There was a boat lying off with a boat's crew in it and two men were on the whaleback. There was a fisheries vessel a little off—they told me they had the last of our radio calls—and I reckoned they were Scrubs by the jabber they were making. I told them to get me off her and they took me aboard. I was still lucky. If I'd been picked up by a ship out of Hull I reckon the skipper would've made me work my passage seeing there wasn't much the matter with me.

'As they took me off I could see there wasn't much left of her aft of the foredeck. Her bridge was gone, winch, boats, boatdeck, all gone and she'd opened up aft. But she was all right at the whaleback where I was—I kept wondering after if I would've stayed there fifteen hours but for Joe Fisher's half bottle.'

Punch was flown home from Iceland and when he told his tale there was a small sensation which survived a day or two in the press. At the enquiry Punch's report made no difference to things and the loss of the *Frances* with all hands save one was duly attributed to the skipper's negligence. There was nothing said about the fitness of a man to command a ship when, apart from an hour or two snatched below four or five times, he had spent four days and four nights on the bridge.

The priest who made it his business to enlighten trawlermen and their families on religious matters spread a few words of comfort among the next of kin of the lost men. He also opened a fund for them.

There are no pensions available on the Fish Dock except those earned from premiums paid to private insurance companies, but out of the reimbursement which they recovered for the ship- wreck from the underwriters the owners did send in a thousand pounds, worth about two hundred and fifty kit of fish on a good market. Thus they added to the fund what was expected of them, and with the money already collected from other trawlermen and the public, each of the next of kin was paid off for her man at the rate of nearly three hundred pounds.

Punch took a settlement based on what a full trip might have fetched, a free set of gear, and a backhander of thirty pounds whose origin he never discovered. Being unmarried he did three things; he drank up his backhander; he gave his mother the main part of his lay and he took himself and his new gear to sea in a 'big boat'. He wanted no more of trawlers. 'But I couldn't stand it,' he said.

'What was the matter, Punch? Were you getting bloody bed sores?'

'No—those lads work hard enough, though not like us silly bastards. No, it wasn't that. But I got to dreaming about fishing. Every time they called me for my watch I used to wonder if there was fish on deck. I used to get so miserable that when we paid off in Cardiff at the end of the voyage I didn't sign again. I came back up here. Daft, eh?'

# CHAPTER 18

# Ten Days' Work—Hauling—Rum

Aft, the third hand was holding a crowbar and stood under the boatdeck swaying to the roll of the ship and with eyes forward on the window at the wing of the bridge. One of his watchmates —for the third hand and his two men had not long turned out and were said to be 'on watch', meaning they were responsible, among other duties, for heaving in the gear at hauling time until the doors surfaced when we all set to—Colville, then, left the pounds, knocked out his knife, took off his cotton gloves which he laid on the winch cylinder, and put on mittens.

He went behind the winch and opened the stop valve to pass steam into the cylinders. He let it idle and warm up and then, reducing speed so that it was just turning over, he slid into their sockets with the clutch lever the two heavy blocks which connected the fore warp drum with the mechanism of the drive. He shouted out a word and the window went up.

'Knock out!' the call went aft.

The third man stepped a pace under the boatdeck, leaned over the gunwale and pulled out the 6-inch pin holding the leaf of the warp block in place. He set the turned-up end of the crowbar under the hinged leaf using the swivel where the block joined its chain as his fulcrum, he leaned his body back, holding the top end of the bar easy at arm's length. He took care to work on the fore side of the fairlead which carried the chain over the gunwale, clear of the annihilating arc of the block and chain should it jump away from the warps. He tugged carefully at the end of his bar and suddenly the block, freed, slammed into the ship's side. The fore warp whipped past us, gutting in the pounds, and then stood off from the side steady, leading away aft and out suspended from the gallus sheave. Colville spun his brake free and heaved in a few fathoms, the cold winch labouring under the load. He slowed and slipped in the clutch blocks of the after warp drums, released that brake and wound in the two wires together. The winch picked up the weight and he opened the steam to full speed.

Now the revolving drums must not be left unattended as they wind up the wire for, left alone, they will wind in so that the winch does the lightest possible work. The turns of wire would go on to the big spools foul. There would be overlays which would flick off the piled-up coils of wire and be held fast, as slack bights, by other turns wound in. Not only would the lay of the wire be nipped and the warp itself weakened but there could well be trouble during the shoot as they ran off. The warps must go out clear. Therefore the wires must be passed evenly from side to side of the drums, each turn lying, as far as possible, alongside the one before it. To do this two pairs of vertical rollers are mounted on the foreside of the winch and secured in a frame to a rack and pinion, the whole under the control of a big handwheel placed in the centre of its after side. The warps, led from the winch between these rollers, can then be taken as required both ways across the drums. It needs a strong hand on the wheel to heave the warps against their natural pull right up to the flanges of the drums, and 'winding it up', as the operation is called, especially when the weather is drifting inboard—and when the other hands are taking five minutes in the warm of the galley— is much disliked.

We all wondered then, in a ship where I was afloat with old Ben, why after five days' work he began to volunteer to go to the winch at every haul though the weather was fresh and freshening. On that trip we carried a pleasurer in the skipper's berth, a nice old bird who told us when we were yarning on the bridge during the run off that he was a colonel in the army. Now the winch of a trawler is set just forward of the skipper's berth, and the winch-man, standing on his grating, can use that bulkhead as a convenient backrest. In the bulkhead is a port, a little round window through which the skipper gets his daylight. I found out why Ben had been acting the unselfish shipmate as soon as he went for his watch below. I was winding in myself when the hundred-

fathom mark came inboard. Over the roar of the winch I heard the
sound of the port opening. Out stretched a fist and in it was a
tumbler, about a third of a pint and full to the brim with rum.
The Colonel's voice came through clear, 'Drink that.'

Ben was below two hauls; I took them both and boarded him
discreetly when he turned out.

'Don't tell a word. I'll split 'em with you,' he said dishonestly.
'There isn't a dram aboard the bastard save what's left in the
Colonel's bond.'

He went to terrific trouble to hide what he and I were getting.
'I'll go,' he said when it came to hauling time and another should
have taken the winch. 'My head's aching. I need the air.'

Next I went there fast as though by mistake. But our time was
up. 'The bastard's up to something,' said the third hand as he saw
Ben preparing to hurry out of the mess deck at hauling time.
'Stay here, Ben. I'm going this time.'

'Aye, have a look, third hand,' said the fish room man.

Later in the pounds the third hand said quietly to us. 'Ye pair
of bastards.' That was all he said, but from then each man worked
his turn at the winch. But even at that Ben had not shot his bolt.
We had aboard an experienced decky learner, a good trawler lad,
nearly a man and well used to winding in the gear.

'I'll go,' Ben said to him affably after the discrediting, 'You
don't want to be drinking that stuff, snacker.'

'Why, you old swine,' shouted the young man, outraged at his
shipmate's impudence who in the worst of weather had never from
good will raised a finger to help him.

'That's a rude boy,' said Ben to us at large as the lad went
forward to heave the gear.

When we saw the fifty-fathom marks come aboard we knocked
out our knives and changed into our mittens and in a few more
seconds the mate took over the winch from Colville. The pounds
emptied as each one of us went to our place. At the fore gallus
Ginger cleared the big door chain and stood at the gunwale
holding the bight of it in his hands. The ship turned and the
weather which had been from our quarter came in across her
beam; the two warps drew away from the ship's side. Then in

the pool of light just over her side I saw the dark shape of the fore door rising fast to the surface.

'Coming up!' Ginger shouted and the mate slowed the winch. The door banged up the ship's side and as its brackets rose above the gunwale Ginger dropped the end of his chain neatly through them and hooked it back to the gallus leg. The mate unshipped his fore clutch and heaved up the after door. Both warps were unclipped from their doors and he hove them in to the drums.

The wires crackled like dried straw as they rode through the turning sheaves. They shone like brand-new wires under the lights, but the newness was deceptive for every strand in them had been ragged. They were polished between the doors and the trawl by the constant chafe of the sea bed which split the top strands of the lay into thousands of razor-sharp points. It was these little needles running fast over the sheaves which made the swish. We used to handle them with care for the rags in them could easily rip away the flesh of our fingers. Then the big bobbins and brackets of the Dan Lenos rose from the sea and came tight to our galluses.

The mate cut the steam off the winch and disconnected the drums. Clipped to each bracket, both fore and aft, were ropes whose ends we took to the winch through the fairleads on the engine-casing in her waist. The winch hove and the ropes came inboard and closed the mouth of the trawl. It was lifted by these quarter ropes right to the gunwale. When we hove the ropes all in we found wire strops at their ends fastened to the big bobbin wire. Aft we slipped a hook from the gallus into the strop and into the fore one we hooked the jilson. They hove up on the winch and the bobbin wire with its massive beads rose in over the gunwale and was dropped to the deck.

All of us took net hooks, double-ended s-shaped hooks which fitted the palm of the hand; we fell on the net, driving the hooks freely into the mesh and dragging back with all the weight of arms and shoulders. We waited for her to roll to the weather, down to the net in the water; we grabbed in handfuls of slack mesh and held on as she lifted, then more slack as the gunwale went down again, fleeting what we had gained round our feet.

The bellies of the net stretched out to the weather and then a spotlight flashed on from the bridge and the skipper searched the darkness over the side for his cod-ends. We saw them laying out in the waves, moving to the sea—the white stomachs of the live fish were gleaming and flickering in them.

The mate worked at the fore end of the trawl and the bosun aft, both pulling back on the lacings of the bellies. As she rolled down to the net the mate called to us, 'He—eave!' and then, 'Ho—old it!'. Some mates used to curse the net as we tried to take the fleets inboard. Sometimes the cod-ends would not float, had no buoyancy in them—haddock by itself, with no cod there, used often to come up as dead weight, for oxygen seemed to be easily pressed out of their bodies; and sometimes we trawled up a bag of 'duffs', globes of compacted weed, a grey oatmeal sort of colour, which looked like big puddings. Then it took all our strength to fleet the net inboard.

Sometimes in bad weather, when the ship lay vulnerable across it as we took our gear aboard, big green rollers used to break in over her waist. We would look up at them advancing on to us, the crests almost out of range of our floods, overpowering masses of water; and one would catch her slow footed, and someone, seeing what must happen, would cry out. We would jump for the engine-room casing, or the bridge ladder, or the winch, and hang on while the deck where we had been working filled with sea and all the fleets of net we had gained inboard would be swilled back over the side. It was too easy to be taken into the sea with outrunning net; many have gone this way though a lucky handful have had the amazing fortune to be floated back inboard as she laboured to the next sea.

Then when the 'square' of the net, the canopy over the trawl mouth, was rove aboard our hooks dug into the great sleeve of the bellies, and we began to draw the floating cod-ends towards us. Hundreds of gulls screamed as they swooped about ready to get at the fish, and some daring ones stood awash on the mesh of the cod-ends trying to tear out the fish from inside.

'Close 'em up!' the mate called. He and the bosun drove their thighs at the net spread over the gunwale, forcing the belly lacings together; we with our hooks helped them to bundle the net up.

'Snottler!' (The name of a rope.)

The two men leaned their bodies out over the gunwale and the mate passed the whipped end of the rope between the ship's side and the bellies of the net. The bosun sought under the net for the rope's end and drew it to himself as the mate let him have slack. They slipped a timber-hitch around the bellies, dropping the hitch as far down to the water as possible. The winch was already running, the bight of the snottler let to it through a fairlead.

'Heave!' came the mate's shout.

Colville at the winch barrels ran three turns of his rope on to them, the timber-hitch came tight and the bellies were drawn smoothly inboard. The mate and bosun passed the snottler's other end, made their hitch and the mate shouted as one word, 'Le'go—heave!' The winchman kept it running hard, Colville flicked his turns off the barrel, a hand at the fairlead cast the snottler bight out of it and dropped in its new hauling part, Colville ran on his turns and another fleet of bellies came in. So working end after end they raced the bellies inboard until we had the double mesh of the cod-ends coming over the gunwale. One more heave and the mate called for the bag-rope. He and the bosun passed this wire which was covered with a soft hemp padding around the cod-ends.

The bag was now strained out of the water and our fish had all tumbled into its extreme end; it was bulky and heavy, almost too much for the double mesh as the *Steerwell* lifted her gunwale to the swell and the bag drew clear of the supporting sea.

'Tackle!' he called.

A hand overhauled slack through its sheaves and carried the heavy thing on his shoulder to where the mate was waiting. He hooked it into the two eyes at the ends of the bag-rope. Even while hooking in the big block he shouted, 'Tack—ool!'. The winch roared and over on the lee side the hand on the tackle haul took in the slack of the falls and caught the weight of the bag on the winch. As he hove back the suspended bag swung along the side from her waist to the shrouds of the mast, the tackle falls shortened until they were lifting vertically and the bag came streaming up; the fish made a loud rustling noise as they were lifted clear and packed together and then the bag swung gently and heavily to rest against the stops.

CHAPTER 19

# The Tenth Day—Clewing Up

After ten days' work there was not much strength left in us; what there was we saved as best we could to keep the work going at the same speed. In the mess deck we sat quiet at dinner but I remember Colville pushing away his plate, and saying: 'Don't ye think the bastard's had enough?'

One or two spoke of the chance of getting her gear aboard and starting our run home. 'He's got to go home,' said the third hand, 'the team's knackered.'

From about the seventh day of work in a trawler the danger which always hovers around her begins to close in. This is the time when the ships and men are most prone to the terrible number of accidents which afflict the industry. The judgment of all hands is spoiled as fatigue becomes permanent, and concentration and alertness are no less casualties on deck than on the bridge. It is then that gear is most likely to be fouled, then that fingers and hands are most likely to be smashed, and torn, then that trawlermen may most easily be dismembered and ships lost. The speed of the machinery and the mechanical gear which the men use to help them can only be increased to the pace at which they can reasonably work it. If it is pushed beyond that point more men will be needed or else the equipment will have to be improved. I believe that trawlermen sustain a pace of toil as high as any man who earns a wage for himself and a dividend for a shareholder, and anyone can see (that is if he takes the trouble to make a trip in an old trawler from say Milford Haven, then another trip in a new one from Hull—but a sociologist who did that would have to be unusually keen on his field work—I say anyone can see that the speed at which fishing is carried on has been formidably increased and without a total alteration and re-design of the gear cannot be notched higher.

After dinner we hauled.

'Jesus, make the greedy bastard go home.' We made two bags of the catch and the mate stepped back and looked up at the bridge before bending to tie the cod-line. The bridge window slammed down: 'Get it aboard, Ernie!' the skipper shouted and we all looked at one another and were thankful.

Clewing up is one of the moist poignant moments of a trawler-man's life. I am not remembering falsely now when I say that it is then, for a few seconds, that he recalls his relationship to all the men who live ashore, to all those who do not have to go out there. I can easily bring back to mind, when I think of the number of times I have been part of a crew given the order to clew up, the sweetness of that moment's thought of friends, men and women, I knew ashore. I had no wife when I went fishing, but I am certain that the need of all the sweetness to be had from a wife came then into the minds of married trawlermen. Long after I had parted from him and was floating in other ships I re-membered the run ashore I took with a hand who offered me a free bed when I was new to the industry in Hull.

We docked at the end of the winter on an evening tide and hurried the taxi over the railway yards to get to his home. He was so pressed for time that we stopped only a minute in Pine's to drink a glass of rum while the barman brought up six bottles of beer for us to take away.

'I'll come on later,' I said, for I did not want to stand in the way of his immediate affection for his wife.

'No,' he said, 'there's plenty of time for that. You come and meet our lass. We'll get under the lee of the stove.'

We came to the door of his little house in the terrace and I was slow to pay off the driver to give my shipmate time to embrace the girl who answered his knock and his call through the door. We went through a little passage into the sitting room where a fire burnt up brightly with plenty of red coals and small blue and red flames. Everything was in order, clean and neat, and covering the big square table was a thick and warm-looking cloth. There was a pile of children's clothing on a ledge in a corner by the fireplace ready for mending or ironing. It was as snug in there as a trawler's fo'c's'le but it had all the comfortable equipment for living which we were short of.

We took off our gear and sat down while his wife made tea for us. She stepped back continually into the sitting room through the opened scullery door to tell us something, to make a joke, to keep herself in the conversation. She was well made and friendly and I enjoyed being envious of his possession of such a wife. After a time we sat up to the table with the beer poured into glasses which she polished before setting in front of us, and played dominoes and then rummy for very small stakes. We two shipmates were poor hands at the games and I can laugh now at the pleasure with which she took our sixpences. All I remember of those two days ashore is that we spent them in the ordinary pleasant ways of staying alive. We joined her and her children for an hour or more of shopping; they invited me with them to see a film; of the three evenings, two we spent at his house and one in a walk about the city to a few bars. In the freezing early morning of the third day we left and in the taxi he said to me, 'I hate this bastard life. I hate leaving them.'

But that man still goes. I know something of what men who are married to women they love think about when the order comes, at the end of a five-day voyage and ten days' work, to clew up and go home.


We hove the trawl inboard aft and forward, clambering over the fish to rive the worn-out bellies and cod-ends clear of the fish pounds where the final haul lay to be gutted and put below. We dropped the trawl doors into their place, tight between the galluses and the bulwarks. The winch was constantly in tremendous motion as the hands working aft and forward took their leads to it to heave the bobbins into position, tight into the rail where they could be made fast with lengths of light chain. Even as the last of the gear came in over the side we heard in the bridge the ring of the telegraph, the engineer answering the skipper's call for full speed. She began to pick up revolutions and I watched the horizon swing past the turning bow until she had put the glim of the winter sun ahead of her and we were bound south with the breeze from the north-west chasing us and shivering the tops off the seas running with us.

The bridge window opened again: 'Come up here, one of you.'

All hands stopped work and looked at the mate.

'Y'all look about knackered,' he remarked. 'Do ye feel tired, Punch? D'ye want to climb up there?'

Colville shouted, 'Take my tobacco. I don't like to see a hand not smoking while he's watching us work.'

Once after a terribly hard trip off the west coast of Iceland in winter I was ordered on to the bridge to steer her along when the skipper set her off homeward bound. As I took off my frock and mittens in the galley and filled a mug of tea to take up with me, I relished my good fortune. In the bridge it was warm and dry, and though it was no more comfortable than any other work-shop filled with technical apparatus, still it was a great luxury to me, fresh off the soaking and freezing deck. The skipper gave me the course, and then—with face nervous looking, dark with dirt and the ten days' beard, eyes not fully open and red with the closeness of total fatigue, in their corners the dried up lubrication of the eyes gathered like scabs—that tired man went below to his berth.

'Call me,' he said, 'in three hours.'

I got myself into an easy position behind the wheel, felt for her balance on course and laid out my tobacco and papers in the little box handy for the steersman. Then I looked out of the window and around the horizon and then down on my shipmates 15 feet below. The gutting pounds seemed too full of men; three extra hands, the last watch below, were working there, for on the last haul of the trip and the clew-up it is the custom for all hands to be called.

On that trip, so foul was the ground over which we had been working that the gear had taken damage on nearly every tow. To keep the fish coming aboard the skipper had ordered us to prepare a second trawl for fishing from the ship's port side. We were then forced, each time repairs had to be done, to reeve the warps and their heavy accoutrement to the gear on the other side. Then with that gear shot away, we had to set about the damage in the one just hauled. Our work was made heavier because we had a full set of pound boards rigged on both sides of the foredeck over which we had to clamber like slow hurdlers and over which we had to rive the mass of spare net, and other gear from the net hold, to the places where it was needed. And while we mended our nets we had an eye on the fish pounds where on both sides of the ship a tide of ungutted fish was rising against the efforts of two hands and a snacker to deal with it, the only three who could be spared from the mending. Forward of the mast and under the break of the fo'c's'le a pile of net too damaged to be worth mending was growing, which had been replaced on the trawl by sections of new net; and coiled down as far out of the way as possible were the many lengths of cast-off cable worn into sharp wire rags.

After three days of working the two sides of the ship, piled on to that first seven days when we could not get clear of damage, we began to feel overwhelmed. Everyone's fingers, chafed raw from net and fish, painful right into the quick of the nails, were hardly capable of work. Everyone's muscles were too far strained and the watch below could not be called sleep but a plunging relinquishment of consciousness. And from those pits we were dredged up all unwilling to return to the deck. Now I watched them through the bridge windows while they gutted and put below fish accumulated from six or seven hauls.

In three hours the decks were clear of fish and the holds battened down; over the hatches cowhides were stretched and fastened by a rope taken round them under the lips of the hatch coamings and hove tight on the winch. The catch was aboard and secured.

I called the skipper and he came into the bridge and in silence noted the light of the cape we were putting on our beam; he set me a new course and returned below. I watched them at work on the floodlit deck making everything fast for the run home. There were more than 60 pounds boards to be taken from the slotted deck stanchions and stowed in their compartment; the men could scarcely carry them forward. Where ten days before one of those strong men had been quite easily able to shift each board about and secure it in its place, now it was as much as two could manage to joggle it clear of the slots and labour forward with it. In the now following wind the hands were able to get about the deck without their frocks, but even unencumbered they looked slow, like sick men. Four were engaged in slashing the old trawls from the bobbin wires, stopping from time to time to rub their knives on the steel to bring up the edge so that the effort of cutting through the seizings of yarn was reduced. Then they cut out the ruined and worn out parts of the net and stretched what was good in the rigging, up and down the shrouds, to dry before stowing it away.

Now that we were well clear of the grounds we could put our accumulated rubbish over the side without fear of its being trawled up and badly fouling other men's gear, or even our own on another trip. The third hand and two more carried the rusting coils of torn cable aft; they did not touch them with their hands but passed hanks of yarn through the coils and dragged them like that. Then right at the stern of the ship, through the after hawse-pipe, well clear of her screw and her rudder, they paid it away; the big coils flaked off quick and dangerous looking as the sea caught the weight of the wire and ran it off against the way of the ship.

All this work was slowly done; the ship began to take on the spare, stripped appearance of a trawler on passage. Then at last the mate stood in the middle of the foredeck and looked about him. Two of the men were leaning against the warp bollards at the foot of the mast, others walked aft to the galley and mess room. The mate waved to me to switch off the floods and they quit the darkened deck. I was able to see better into the night ahead.

Though I had clewed up many times it happened that I had never before seen a team toiling at the job from the height of the bridge, a job which requires the last remaining ounce of their stretched-out energy. I can remember that I was grieved to see everyone's vitality so seriously depleted.

We were sitting in the mess room with the wonderful feeling of a completed trip—for the run home was hardly accounted work after the fish room had been filled.

'Go down to my berth, snacker,' the mate said, 'and bring up what's under the pillow.'

He returned in a moment with a full bottle of rum and the cook brought thick little dram glasses to the table. We were tired, but now that we knew that during the next days our full need for sleep was going to be satisfied, and now that here in front of us we had the prospect of easy conversation and a glass or two of rum, none were anxious to go forward. We would let the demand for bed overhaul us, though it was going to be no less irresistible for that. The taste of the liquor—which for days we had forgotten —was good, bringing appetites to life, as it went harsh over the tongue. Rum drunk for pleasure, instead of trying to find in the bottom of the glass a few more pounds of energy and a breath or two more of spirit. The third hand asked, 'Is someone going to relieve Punch?'

'Damn him,' said Colville and raised his glass to his absent shipmate.

# CHAPTER 20

# The Run Home

As a dayman, that is a man who keeps no watch, life in a trawler on a homeward passage is good. There were three of us, the fish-room man and we two snackers, and we worked from eight in the morning until half past four with whoever could be spared of the three men keeping the bridge watch. Thus during the day it was us or the cook who was first in touch with the latest bridge gossip: the state of the fish market, the names of the ships who had landed, and so on; all valuable information when it came to estimating our probable lay.

The first two days homeward bound we spent our time tidying up the net hold and preparing for the next trip. We tallied the gear and net remaining aboard and began to fix sections of new trawl. We worked at an easy pace, taking care to fold and lash and coil what was down there very neatly before fastening the identifying labels.

The other snacker or myself was sent aft frequently to see if the cook had any tea; it was a pleasure to go through without hurry the simple movements of filling needles, or braiding, or lacing, or splicing rope and wire, knowing that each job was an essential part of the complexity of making a whole trawl and of the operation of trawling.

During the afternoon of the second day the wind freshened to a gale just on our starboard quarter as we altered course to cross the North Sea. Sometimes she rolled away from a sea and dipped her rail, scooping inboard tons of water whose swirling tops splashed across the mess-deck porthole.

'She's filling her gauge glass,' said the second engineer. 'He'll have to ease the bastard in.'

'Nay, he wants the tide. He'll let her run.'

The mess tables were rigged with bad-weather battens and each man's place at the table was sectioned off into a little square so that he could control his plate, and so that the cook's platters of food, the bottles of sauce, the butter, the sugar, the salt and pepper and his own pot of tea would not be distributed into his lap.

'You'd better take them some tea on the bridge,' the third hand said to me. I filled a jug and clambered up through the galley skylight and on to the engine-room casing. I could see the seas mounting towards the little ship's stern, appearing out of the darkness, sometimes so high that the slope to their tops, streaked white with the spume, vanished away overhead out of the range of the decklights' glim. She lifted her stern, rolled down to leeward and they would pass like express trains leaving her to fall into the valley, the water eddying and seething round her while she prepared herself for the next. There was a tremendous noise.

I made my way forward past the funnel, holding on where I was able, and worked myself up the weather ladder into the bridge.

'Bastard, eh,' said the mate. 'Did you get wet, snacker?'

At the wheel the steersman was working hard; coming into his hands was the feel of the *Steerwell*'s track through the gale. As each sea ran her down and passed under her it threw a moment of force on to her quarter whose result, unchecked, would have put her broadside to the weather at the risk of being overwhelmed. His task, as she lifted, was to force her to leeward on the path of the wave and then, at that precise instant one only learns to gauge from hundreds of hours at the wheel of a ship, to let her come back to the weather and on to her course as she sagged down the trough. If he applied too much rudder to leeward she could be thrown on the other tack and swept by the sea from her other side. Each onrushing sea set him a fresh set of problems of thrust and compensation, and all the time he, a sensitive human computing apparatus, had to seek the average of the ship's course in the reflection in the overhead mirror of the swinging compass card. I rolled him a cigarette, lit it and passed it to him, then set down handy for him a pot of tea.

There were three more in the bridge, for I noticed the skipper leaned against a leeside window with the mate and the other hand of the watch. The only light came from the dim compass bowl and was reflected in the deckhead steering mirror. The curtain between the bright little radio cabin and the bridge was drawn but we could hear the operator oscillating his set, finding his way through the streaming morse signals. There was no other noise except the slight mechanical noise of the shaft of the wheel in its bearings as the turns were applied to it and spun off. All up there were wondering if the skipper would keep her going in the freshening gale or if he would run her up into the weather and dodge in safety for a few hours until the depression passed clear of us.

I once had a friend in a ship commanded by a very young man who was making his third trip as skipper. We heard after it was all over that homeward bound in the North Sea in a following gale he had let her run on too long. Their trip had been full of trouble and the young skipper had worked two extra days on the grounds to try to fill his ship. He reckoned that he had no time in hand if he was to catch the tide he was chasing at Hull for the market he wanted.

Skippers are under intolerable pressure from owners for these have no hesitation in depriving a skipper for months of his living and his ship if he fails to make the profit which they expect from him. The experienced men have the strength and confidence to put up resistance but the young ones, fresh in command, are more vulnerable. He had therefore kept her before the wind when no doubt caution and his knowledge of the sea must have told him that it was time to turn her and stem that terrible weather. And then there was one sea which was too much for her. She broached, went broadside and could not clear the water that broke aboard. The sea hove her down and she went with all hands save four. They managed to clear a raft and from it they were picked up some hours later by a passing ship.

We ran on through the night. The skipper remained silent. In his mind there must have been the constant question: whether to make a fast passage, risking the weather, or to heave her to in safety? We left him to his continuing calculations and applied ourselves as lookouts on the gale, each to his own bridge window.

When it was time to change the watch he rang down to the engineer for slow speed so that the relieving men could scramble in safety across the deck. It was then that I left the comfortable little bridge and went forward to sleep. He must have been looking for the last of us to duck into the fo'c's'le for once inside we felt the vibrations of full speed return and she picked up again her plunging motion ahead.

By next morning the gale had overhauled us and we were left riding on its swell. It was the last day of the trip and now we were to make the *Steerwell* a yacht.

The cook and galley boy threw the coconut mats from the after accommodation out on deck where they were scrubbed and rinsed and hung out on the boat deck to dry in the breeze. All the cook's pans were burnished and the bright parts of the stove; the linoleum was washed down and polished; the paint in the mess room was cleaned of the stains which our shoulders and heads had made on it as we leaned back from our meals, and all the brasswork, the frames of the portholes and the handrails, was polished.

'Keep your bleeding hands off the brightwork, Steve,' said the cook to me, not unkindly but pointing out that he did not want to do his work again, when I went aft to get tea for the men on deck.

We cleaned the outside brass and especially the 6 feet tall engine-room ventilators, big-mouthed scoops which could be swung to the wind when the engineer wanted more draught. We rubbed off the accumulations of salt and the green deposit laid on them by the weather and then polished them until they glinted in the winter sunshine. The watch was responsible for the bridge, and that navigational workshop began to gleam. They burnished up the steel controls of the sounding and direction-finding apparatus, all the brasswork of the compass mounting, the bridge clock and even the ashtrays. The windows were cleaned and polished and finally they scrubbed the gratings laid over the floor and put down the newly washed mats.

On deck we rigged the donkey and with a full head of water from that pipe we washed her down from forward to aft, scrubbing her deck planking with a caustic solution which left the pine white and fresh looking, though still scarred from the battering of the tremendous and punishing work which is done there. From one or two corners we extracted a limp and decayed codling or a fish liver, flotsam on deck from the previous night's gale which had swept all the other rubbish through the scuppers. Finally we cleaned and polished our own quarters. When we had finished she looked a picture from forward to aft.

'It's a bastard,' said Punch, 'the way we put these ships in dock. The only time they're fit to live in is when we're climbing off them.'

What he said was true, and I often wondered why trawlermen who spend usually no more than a few weeks in a ship cherish them so much. One thing is certain: it was not fear of the owners which made us return their property to them, not only filled with profit, not only in full readiness for another expedition, apart from stocking up with stores, but bright from the care we had lavished on it. I saw no ship of any other class look like these as they went up the estuary into dock, in fact I never knew a mate in a dockbound merchantman give more than superficial attention to the appearance of his ship. No, I believe there is something of a practical perfectionist about a trawlerman. Everything he does when he sets about his job is stamped with the mark of a first-class professional: it is not surprising, then, that he gives heed to finish, to the rounding off of a trip so that his ship steams into the Humber, even on a dark winter's evening when no one can see it, in as perfect shape as he can manage.

In the late afternoon we crossed a clear line in the sea, a marked division between the grey sea and the muddy alluvial water of the Humber, and soon we picked up the light ship and the line of buoys leading us into the river. The motion of the ship came off her as we moved under the lee of the Spurn, the flats which form the estuary's north arm. In the fo'c's'le I bathed in the enamelled tub; it was first filled with cold water and then made as hot as you liked by the valve controlling the jet of steam piped forward from the engine-room. Two of us shared the little bathroom, one shaving and cleaning such teeth as he owned, the other soaking off the dirt from the body and helped by his mate with a scrub over the broad of the back. The fresh feel of clean clothing was good even though the shore gear in which we had embarked was none of the best and we could all have done with an ironing and a pressing.

One by one we gathered aft in the mess room. The weather-lined and in the main good-natured faces were smoothed almost out of recognition by the mouthfuls of false teeth they had inserted. I was to meet trawlermen in other ships who would not wear false teeth—old Ben was such a man—but who had honed their gums to an edge sharp enough to masticate their food. Not the shoregoing but the working face, where the teeth were in short supply, seemed to suit a man better. I never liked the stretched out lips breaking into a smile over those terrible white dentures as much as I liked the dropped-in mouths whose weather-hard grimness could be lit by the best of toothless smiles.

I took my last pot of tea on deck and sat aft on the lee side of the bitts looking out over the river coast of Lincolnshire, now traced by sparse lights once we had put the gleam of Grimsby astern. The shine of some of the flats could be seen as the tide made over the mud. A hand came aft from the bridge and the pair of us carried out the last job of the homeward voyage before putting her into dock.

Right at the aftermost part of the ship, on the taffrail, a little clock was clamped. Clipped to it on its seaward side was a bronze wheel and streaming away from that at the end of a round braided rope, forty or more fathoms astern of us, was a small propeller made to revolve by the pull of the ship through the water. The revolutions of the screw were transmitted through the braided line to the wheel which spun fast or slow according to the speed of the ship. The bronze wheel, charged with the kinetic energy which it derived from the screw astern, maintained an almost steady pace. Its revolutions, counted by the clock mechanism, were converted and recorded on its face as numbers of sea miles. Thus we always knew our distance through the water, one essential factor among others—moved as we also were by tide and wind—which would tell us our position over the sea's bed. Now we unhitched the line and padded it round a stanchion and overboard, pulling in the propeller made so heavy by the speed of the ship that hauling it needed our combined strength, and paying away what we had gained around the stanchion to let the turns accumulated in the line spin out. Then when we had the propeller inboard we heaved back the now cleared line, coiled it down and made it fast on the taffrail alongside the clock, ready for streaming on her next run off to the grounds.

The voyage was nearly done. Upstream of all the port's main docks the skipper turned her to seaward to stem the flooding tide and we edged into the quay, the Bullnose, outside our own dock. But there an indignity was waiting for us which we could have done without.

I've never liked a Customs Officer and I've even found most of them an ill-mannered, policeman-like set of men. Five of them now swarmed over the *Steerwell*'s side. Though dressed in naval rig they were no more like seafarers than detectives are, riding through the streets in a patrol car and looking for trouble. Two went on to the bridge to check our store of bonded goods.

'The bastards'll get a bottle from the old man,' said Colville.

Two came forward into the fo'c's'le where we stood by our bags. The most that any of us could have been carrying hidden as smuggled stuff was a half pound of shag and a hundred or so cigarettes, for there was not enough rum left forward of the bridge to moisten a postage stamp. But from the way they eyed us you might have thought that we were concealing sufficient free trade to cause another crisis in the balance of payments.

'Let's have a look in your bag,' said one, a short sandy-eyebrowed man who failed to sweeten his order to Punch with a smile.

'We live in here,' said Punch. 'Take off your cap, will you.' The eyebrows came together the fraction of an inch, then he

I                            137

removed his hat. Nothing in Punch's bag, I said to myself, if that's the tack he's on.

'Take it out, please,' said the officer.

'It's you who wants to look it over,' Punch replied, 'You get it out. My rags too mucky for you to touch?'

The rummager nodded to his mate and he, clearly a junior, extracted a filthy smock and a pair of fearnoughts, caked about the seat and the crutch with the muck of the fish pounds. He poked an arm deep in the sausage shape of the bag, then sandy brows called him off.

'We're only doing our job,' he said plaintively, appealing to all of us.

'Stop it, you're bringing tears to my eyes,' said Punch.

Colville said, 'Why don't you go and charge the gaffer duty on his bastard fish?' The searchers left the fo'c's'le.

'Psychology—that's what you want. I knew the bastard wouldn't look far if I put the needle in him. I've half a pound of shag for our old man and half a pound for myself in there.'

Punch restowed his bag and we went on deck to warp her through the lock basin.

# CHAPTER 21

# Settling—Manning—the Sack

I left my lodgings early on the following morning and walked about the centre of the town after breakfast. It was very pleasant to sit down in coffee shops and pass the time waiting for my lay. Though nearly penniless after settling bed and breakfast I felt rich with the thought of the earned money to come.

It was years since I had developed the style of life of those seafarers who make up for their exclusion, blockaded in ships by the wilderness of the sea, with an excess of profligacy ashore. I make no argument here for such a pendulum of a life, half the time anchorite and half hedonist. It has its compensations: a wide and continuously replenished circle of friends; a working knowledge of numbers of the coasts of the world; in many a great, familiar, unscholarly love of books; highly developed powers of talking, no less of listening; great ability with the body which is their main tool, developed all round, not lop-sided as are the bodies of so many workers. Seafarers are also rightly famous as men of warm affection, for with time ashore so limited they cannot afford themselves the luxury of a cold-hearted pose; their enjoyment of the company of all sorts of women, rough or gentle, rapacious or generous, is certainly more acute than most men's, for its intensity is increased by the time they spend without them.

I say all this in modest support of a way of life which I once loved and also in damnation of those who withdraw the hem of their garments a little from seamen; who, for example, write letters in the local press of seaports complaining of some briefly witnessed debauchery of the very men who make the life of the port possible, or who conduct social surveys and come to the conclusion that seamen, and in particular trawlermen, live their lives in such and such a way, spend so much money on this and that, make good fathers, bad husbands and an infinity of similar drivel, who studiously amass all this material and leave it at that, saying nothing of the imponderable debt that landsmen owe to seamen nor even of the debt which seamen owe to landsmen, saying nothing in criticism of those parts of society which having demanded the high-grade skill and experience needed to live in and work ships, not only proceed to reward them meanly but also have the impertinence to make harsh judgments about the men who have such powers. In my biased opinion this whole mess of hypocrites, from the parson who spreads his benevolence about the mission outside the dock gate, to the social scientist working up his data and polishing his statistics and his platitudes and taking in a shipowner or two to make up the weight, all these should come to the contemplation of the poor seamen on whose backs they ride by first removing their hats and then knuckling their foreheads.

I began to make my way to the Fish Dock, down the Hessle Road and under the arches, and soon found myself standing among my shipmates outside the crews' entrance to our company building. All hands had on their best clothing, all were clean and polished. As I came up to them Colville called out, 'Now then, snacker, are you ready to be rich?'

'We made six thousand.'

'You can get your shoes mended now, Colville.'

'He's been done.'

'What for?' I asked.

'My face don't fit,' said Colville.

'He needs sharpening up.'

'Getting too fat.'

'He's got to be rendered down a bit.'

'Bastard, snacker, eh?' said Punch to me in his rough voice. 'This is what we've bloody well asked for.'

'What about the Union?' I asked.

Colville himself it was who went through a pantomime of bribery and corruption, palm raised and outstretched behind his back, forefinger and thumb of the other hand rubbed together in the universal sign for paper money, face thrust forward and spread over it the mockery of the expression of a lickspittle.

'The bastards have worked in with the gaffer.' He spat.

'Nay, snacker, I'll have to enjoy me walkabout while I'm look-ing for another.'

Later Punch told me why we were so weak, why we could not fight against a man being thrown out of his ship.

When the war was over it left behind a severe shortage of food in England, and fish with its concentration of nourishment was sold in the greatest quantities which the trawlers could catch. Voyages were completed quickly for, with almost no fishing done on the grounds during the six years of the war, it was fairly easy for a skipper to find fish. In fact so thick did they team inboard that the main difficulty was to get them cleaned and stowed. Therefore to keep the fish moving below six more hands were added to the deck complement of each ship. At the same time the Hull fleet was greatly expanded and renewed, for many of the trawlers taken over by the Admiralty during the war and now released were run down, and not good enough for the heavy demands of fishing the distant waters. Hence, even with the demobilisation of fishermen from active service and their return to the industry, there was still need for recruitment. Though many came in attracted by the big lays that were taken, at the time of a general food shortage, from the assured high price of fish, there is still no doubt that the crews were in a position to resist hard terms offered by the employers. In fact for once the balance tipped the other way: in an industry where management and labour had by tradition enjoyed the worst of relations the crews were only too willing to rub the owners' noses in the dirt. Tales of scandalous scenes were told with relish around the dock. As sailing time approached there was many a ship where the owners and ships' runners had to implore the men to do their duty and go to sea. But often the ships did not leave the dock until the last of the rum and the money were consumed. An owner, famous on the dock, was once coarsely sent about his business and run off his own ship when, enraged with a reluctant crew, he forecast the end of these junketings and the return of the old order, meaning the restoration of his power to use the sack.

The owners began to build up the manning strength of the

industry by a continuous but discreet infusion of decky-learners. To a certain type of working-class boy from Hull, if he is robust, quick thinking and intelligent, a trawlerman's life seems good when he is confronted with the dilemma of choosing a career and is equipped only with rudimentary education. He might then think that he can either settle back more or less placidly and draw his price as a worker, or he can become a member of an élite with always the prospect of a big lay from a lucky market, and even the dream, not unrealistic, of climbing the bridge ladder and drawing the rewards from the command of his own ship.

The trawlermen themselves paid only brief attention to what was happening, though this is not to say that they did not easily guess what the owners had in mind. The conditions of fishing were still so hard and the rate at which owners expended the men at sea and the men expended themselves ashore so breakneck, that at that time, when a berth in a ship was easy to find they were willing to be disputers. 'We knew what the gaffers were up to,' Punch said to me, 'but the lads wouldn't make a move together.'

Then the food shortage eased, the import of meat increased and the demand for fish slacked, and when times were less urgent and berths were scarcer the owners got ready to re-enforce the voracious conditions of employment which had nearly always been the rule. For a start they cut from the ship's company the six extra hands signed on for the big trips after the war. The men struck but the twelve weeks' struggle which then followed was too much for them. The sheer weight of the money which the owners could call on overwhelmed the strikers. Even though a few of the smaller firms were wound up no real impact was made on the big ones. In fact the wealthy companies took this opportunity to broaden their grip on the industry; monopolisation was concentrated further. And when the striking trawlermen's money was spent their only recourse was to go back to sea.

Punch told me that the owners succeeded in reducing the men's conditions for two reasons. First of all the boys who had been trained to the trawlers were now ready to take their places as fully competent hands—some had already established themselves. They had the habit of a big settlement once or twice a year, they were spurred by the possibility of eventual promotion to the bridge, used to the glamour which surrounds the job in Hull, and rightly proud of their standing among the most expert seamen afloat.

Punch said, 'I never bothered to get ashore. Even when you couldn't find a berth you put up with it. The job looks all right when you've just settled and you're standing in Pine's in front of a dram and you're just off for an afternoon's drift.' (He meant an afternoon of making love.) Moreover the job, once mastered, is absorbing and interesting, an endless source of talk on techniques and fishing triumphs, odd shipmates, fiendish skippers, gales and fine weather. 'It's always the same,' he said, 'they pay off the ships but they never pay off the dock,' meaning once a trawlerman always a trawlerman.

The second reason was the admittedly reckless and uncaring psychology of the fishermen. They knew exactly what was being done to them, they knew the dangerous risks they ran and knowing, they still did not have the patience for reform. For they remembered, when they were in a ship, that they had to live three weeks' shore life in forty-eight hours; and what other time they had ashore was usually the result of the sack. Hence there was not much time, as signed-on men, to construct a union powerful enough to protect themselves, and after getting the sack a man was at too much of a loss to seek the solidarity and support of others. Skippers themselves, at the mercy of the thousand chances of a voyage, are no more secure than the hands. They cannot afford three bad trips in a row. No matter what their reputation, three bad voyages will see them relieved of command for two or three months, and they are prone to try to hold off or change ill-luck by changing men. I remember one trip I made as mate of a ship. When we were steaming up the river after a nearly barren voyage, I asked the skipper what his gear requirements were for the deck. After noting all the supplies he needed, he said, 'You can ship me up a new set of faces forward.'

In all the years I fished, however, I never knew a man seek the aid of the union after being thus deprived of his living. Certainly no one looked to it to force any but the most meagre reforms. It never attacked with success the burning matters of hours, manning and leave ashore. But I do record here my respect for the men who always continued their effort to construct an effective organisation, and I record too my belief that it will only be by strengthening and widening the base they have already laid that a good life will come out of these ships.

On those numerous times when some more than usually heavy demand was thrown at us the only response was a shrug and the comment which I heard more often that I like to recall, 'Well, there y'are.' It is as though we knew when we went back time after time what was in store, but tacitly defied the owners to do their worst. Because many of us were improvident, making up ashore for the life lost at sea, and because we were generous with money to a degree most men never know—giving it freely when going steady in a ship to wives, and to old shipmates whom we caught ashore on their beam ends—we were often in want. When it came to our own turn for the sack our own small savings were soon consumed. It used to come hard then to read in the Hull, and even in the national press, articles which deplored our prodigality and which, of course, seldom failed to draw attention to our supposed exorbitant wages.

# CHAPTER 22

# *The Market—the Lay*

If you were about in West Dock Avenue or in one of the other little streets leading down to the dock at half past three of a morning you would see men dressed for rough toil hurrying down to the market, for every day of the week except Saturday and Sunday an early morning rush of work takes place on the Hull fish market.

On the dockside there are two cafés, one of which is handy for the market. By four-fifteen it is full of men taking mugs of tea or coffee and something to eat before they start to unload the trawlers. There will be four or more ships to handle and each ship will have its own gang of men, 'bobbers', highly specialised stevedores. The ships are warped alongside a pair of small derricks, one for each fish-room hatch, and then unloading starts.

On the dockside hundreds of metal barrels are ranked, each one to contain ten stone of fish. These 'kits' are filled at a terrific speed from the catch. In a kit made fast to the derrick whip, fish is swung out of the trawler's hold, weighed and then shot into the tubs off the scales. Boys barrow the loaded kits into line, crashing them into place. The noise on the dock is terrible, for the bobbers cry out all the time, shouting orders to the men at the derricks, shouting to each other in the fish room—long calls whose rhythm seems to help them keep up their speed. And on the dock is the crash and roll of the empty kits as they are brought forward and filled.

At about six o'clock the mate of the ship comes on to the dock to see the state of the catch. He starts with a bribe of five pounds or more for the foreman of the bobbers; that is so that the man will take the trouble to see the fish caught first—by now some fourteen or fifteen days' old—is out of sight, covered in each kit by some good-looking, nearly fresh stuff. The 'shelfers', those good-sized cod which in the last three days of our work we stretched out in tiers, shelved on beds of ice, have to be set out separately. They are the pride of the trip—for every kit of them we reckon to earn plenty of money. We used to say that a bobber's foreman could make or break a trip simply by the way the fish was displayed on the market.

I remember the first trip I went mate in a ship. It was at Christmas time when all good mates, sure of a berth, take a trip off to be with their families. Christmas and Bank Holidays were the times when second-class men and aspirers took their chance to find a berth. That Christmas we had a bad trip; fish was scarce and we had to work through a set of advancing depressions, getting our gear aboard and dodging our ship off the weather as the gales swept by. We were twenty-seven days out and even at the end of the trip we were off the Humber too late, by minutes only, to make the tide into the Fish Dock.

The mate's mastery of the gear on deck must be taken for granted both by the skipper and the crew; without that he is not worth his passage. Over and above this deck responsibility stands the imperative one of the catch, for the mate is in charge of the stowage of the fish caught. But we had plenty of foul work that trip and as a first-timer I was not up to the deck job. I remember I worked myself almost to my knees to try to keep the gear in order and no doubt I did not put a sharp enough eye on the stowage of the fish. We docked five days late and I had doubts about that fish.

The ship was the oldest of the fleet of a famous pair of brothers on the dock, to whom I have already referred in the early part of my book: a short biographical note about them is not out of place here. Their grandfather was an owner-skipper out of Brixham in Devonshire who moved north to Hull when he realised the rising importance of that seaport. The little firm continued to prosper so that in time the old man's son was able to extract such a fortune from his ships' companies during the days when the energy and the very lives of fishermen were even more expendable than they are now that he was able to set up his own two sons as young gentlemen. Their education was the best that money could buy, and they were well-found with all the equipment for smart young men. But education and massive prosperity did nothing to weaken the strength of their family line. In fact by the time I came to float for them their energy and intelligence, their inherited and vigorous compulsion to expand had lifted them into leading positions in the ring of the most powerful owners on the dock. And as the owners and managers of a family business, not responsible to public shareholders, and themselves not screened behind directors, they reckoned to uphold their authority by a brutal rudeness to the men who went to sea for them. Such were my employers when, at seven o'clock of a dark January morning, I waited beside my kits for one of the brothers to come to inspect his fish.

I had paid a generous bribe to the foreman of the bobbers and he, knowing this was my first trip, had been at great pains to lay out our catch as best he could. The most ancient fish was discreetly out of sight but no one could have declared that what was displayed on top of the kits was in the least appetising. There was nothing about it of the beautiful glittering look of fresh decked cod. The brother marched quickly up and down the ranks of the tubs and then turned to the two who dogged him, his dock manager and his fish salesman.

'Shit,' he said, 'who's the mate?'

No one bothered to look at me but my name was passed.

'Clear him out.'

He strode on and that put paid to my first trip as mate.

The foreman bobber came up to me.

'Don't worry about the bastard,' he said kindheartedly, 'you don't remember Davey Quinn, do you? That were four or five years back. I was landing his trip. Davey was a hard bugger and a bloody good first division mate with it. They had a trip same as yours, five or six days over their time and we landed two thousand kit no better than what we've put ashore today. Young mister comes walking up and down to have a look at it and then he turns on Davey. "Shit," he says. He shouldnt've said that to Davey for he nearly always landed a beautiful trip. Took a real pride in his fish room, did Davey. "Nothing but shit. You'd better have a rest for a trip or two, Quinn," meaning the sack.

' "Aye," said Davey, "that's right. It's shit we've landed. You'd do well to have a closer look at it." '

'And he picked him up nice and easy, turned him upside down just as though the gaffer was a baby, and then he drove him head first into a kit of shelfers and tapped him down on the soles of his boots to make sure he could see what was lying in the bottom. None of us did a thing. It was all over too quick, and anyway Davey was a hard man. But for all that he made a mistake. Davey never got another ship out of Hull and when he took his ticket to Grimsby he found they'd blacked him there too. I heard he's fishing on the west side of Canada now.'

We of the *Steerwell* had not been standing long outside the office when the runner came to the door and told us to go upstairs. The hatch in the pay office wall was open and one by one we signed our receipt for the trip, drawing cash which the pay clerk counted out to us from a pile of notes and coins under his hand.

Punch came down with me.

'You feel rich with all this money,' he said. 'You'd better get your first expenses paid. Wait here will you. The bleedin' runner won't want to see more than one of us at a time.'

I followed into the little office when Punch came out, to see the man who had put me into a ship. The big face was composed, friendly and confident looking, as though to make it clear to me that if the business we were about to do was a little shady then the lapse was on my side; he, so to speak, understood my difficulties.

'Well, then, snacker, did you enjoy herself? Do you want to go back?'

He handed me the pen and I signed for another voyage. I put two notes on the desk.

'That'll be all right, son.'

He put the money carefully into his wallet. I said nothing and thus committed myself to his payroll, that is to the roll of those who paid him. What I had contributed seemed to be enough for as I went out he smiled cheerfully at me.

'Have a good trip.'

I joined Punch outside.

'Bastard, eh. Giving your money away before you're even off the dock.'

We went under the tunnel and at the end of the Avenue turned into Pine's. Punch bought drinks to a table in the bar and we sat down.

'Once,' he observed, 'I read in a newspaper that we're members of the aristocracy of the working class. What the bastard meant who wrote that is that we get paid high. That was one of the times when the price of fish was up in the shops. When that happens they throw the blame at us, see. They send some newspaper writer to sea with us and he gets back after he's spent the trip on the broad of his back, seasick first, then pissed up on the skipper's bond, he gets back and he does his job on us. We're right bloody good lads, see. Hard as nails afloat and ashore. Just rough ignorant trawlermen but men of iron, every finger a marlin spike, see. But also he tells all about the money we earn.

'They always make sure that he does his voyage in a first-division ship with a skipper who's almost a certainty for £6,000 at least. Then at £6 to the thousand for the hands and their bit of liver money, and their wages on top, they settle on about £75 for their three weeks' work. You see how it's done? The price of fish is up and here's us rough men taking up to £30 a week. There's only one thing for them to think, see. And all the thieving bastards who're riding on our backs, all those trawler owners and all those merchants, who're robbing a woman over the price of a pound of filleted cod, they've all got under the lee. I'd like to know how much those scribes get for their tales. Who's dropping in the backhander, eh?'

'How much have you got at the end of the year?'

'Well, I've been coming this way a long time now and I've never made more than eight hundred. By the time you've had the sack once or twice and by the time you've waited while she does a voyage on the slip you won't get in more than ten or eleven. Anyway, I don't reckon a man could stand more than twelve trips, thirteen at the outside. And then you've got trips in the summer when nobody wants the fish. I remember once we put three-quarters of our trip back over the wall and the little bit we landed went to the meal factory. We had a radio call six hours off the dock. The market's down, they said. Not worth landing. Happening all the time. You might work for your liver money and wages and near bugger all else. And then there's the cost of your gear, about £40, and some of us have to keep the runner sweet. What it means is this—you average about a thirteen-hour day, seven days a week from dock to dock and you do it for about six shillings an hour or a bit less. Work it out for yourself when you get promoted spare hand. But you've got to remember this—we're still the aristocracy of the working class.'

Punch weighed up his earnings cheerfully. I never heard that man groan about much for he was a great accepter of things as they were. The fact was that he couldn't be bothered to churn up his anger; even the tax which they took from him he wrote off as an inevitable charge which forces beyond his control exacted as the cost of earning his living.

'Those bastards you read about living on those expense accounts,' he remarked. 'You know, I once did something just for a laugh. I put in to get a tax rebate on the cost of my taxis on sailing mornings.'

' "You can use the public transport," he told me.

"At that time of the bastard night," I said.

' "Well, you can walk to the dock, if you like." '

'I tell you, a bloke like that's no more than a cardboard fish.'

# CHAPTER 23

# *Soundings*

I have tried to set down what I remember of my first voyage in a Hull trawler. One voyage was not like another, although the rhythms of watchkeeping, running off and running home were the same, and though the job itself became so familiar that even now I can lie in bed under the lee of my woman when the breeze is blowing a little fresh over the common, and I can imagine those last few seconds before turning out from a watch below; when one of us three, newly awake, asks the hand who called us: 'What's it doing?' He answers, 'All the time . . .', meaning that the weather is freshening steadily. After our cup of tea, we scramble out on deck and tap the shoulder of the man going below and take from him whatever job he has in hand. I could do them all still, but I know this: I no longer have the stamina for eighteen hours, and ten days of eighteen hours.

There are trips that stand out in my mind. The only violence I ever saw at sea was when I was once in a ship where the skipper was a ferocious gorilla of a man, a known bully. There was a snacker in the crew who he bore a grudge against. There was no reason for the grudge save that the boy made an easy scapegoat for a trip which was going from bad to worse. We others of the crew knew what was happening and all did their best to make his life less miserable, for nothing so riles a man nearing fatigue as to have to put up with a stream of coarse and brutal sneering.

Near the end of our ten days' work I was gutting fish next to him in the pound alongside the fore gallus; the bridge window slammed open.

'What's the matter? Are you feeling tired?'

Someone in the pound said quietly, 'It's you he's at, snacker.'

'I said, are yer feeling tired?' The cruelty in the voice was loud.

The boy tossed the gutted fish in his hand into the wash tank. He straightened up.

'If it's me you're talking to, skipper, I've got a name. Else pull your head in.'

We stopped work.

'Christ, he's coming on deck,' a man said.

The boy threw his knife into the deck, the blade driven into the wood; he walked a step to the gallus. Hanging by its lanyard to a cleat was the big claw spanner, two feet long with a head four inches across, its jaws toothed to hold it to the job, a terribly effective tool. The boy took it in both hands and raised it like an axe over his shoulder. He waited in the clear space around the mast for the man coming across the deck.

'Switch off those floods.' The skipper shouted the order to the radio operator in the bridge.

We in the pounds looked above the glare of the lights to the darkness of the wheelhouse. The mate shouted, 'Leave them alone, sparker.'

The lines of spume blew in across the sea from the dark and gleamed white in the floods, still lit up. Under the cluster of lights on the mast the skipper waited. I wondered if he was too hard, too confident as a brawler to see what we could see. The boy looked frightened, his voice was desperate, he was almost pleading.

'Before you can hurt me, Skipper, I'll bray open your head with this claw.'

But the skipper understood as well as we did the danger that was about on deck.

'Get yer rags off 'er, my lad, when we dock.'

He crossed back over the deck and remounted the bridge ladder. In a short time we set off homeward bound, but save for the orders to the mate the bridge windows stayed shut.

'You did right, snacker, but don't let it go to your head.'

The boy remained silent when we turned back to the fish.

I have been on voyages when luck was so bad that the skipper set about breaking the law. Now I do not intend to argue the rights and wrongs of the fishery protection laws. The facts are these: the old law, still in force when I first voyaged from Hull, put the limit of fishing at an imaginary line running three miles off the coast and parallel with its irregularities. Hence a vessel could legally follow the banks right inside the horns of a bay so long as she remained more than three miles off the nearest land. This freedom was very useful to ships when bad weather invaded their sea area, for if they could run for a bay under the lee of the land where the ground was good they could continue working. In one such bay on the north-west side of Iceland, a very deep indentation in the coast, I have seen as many as forty to fifty ships with their gear down when outside it was blowing nearly a full gale.

In this book I have tried to show what an effective weapon the Granton trawl is. The Icelanders' argument was that with all these ships freely sweeping up the fish on the inshore seabeds they were in danger of losing their staple industry. They maintained also that the inshore fish were young stuff and that too many were slaughtered wastefully in the hunt for cod and haddock big enough for the market. Certainly I cannot remember a haul taken inside the fiord where we did not have to throw a great deal of codling overboard. Icelanders insisted that the fiord and bay banks were being seriously overfished and so strongly did they argue their view before the international tribunal set up to judge the dispute that it was laid down that the three miles' limit was not to run parallel with the coast but was to be measured from cape to cape. Immediately all grounds in the bays and fiords were put out of bounds to foreign fishermen.

But at about this time a great improvement was achieved in the design of trawlers; their power and their ability to work in bad weather were increased. The prohibition on the grounds right inshore still failed to prevent general overfishing on the coast, and although there was very powerful lobbying before the tribunal by British trawler owners, who were supported by certain of their skippers in the assumed role of advisory experts (a role to which they were not entitled because obviously their knowledge of the science of fish conservation was limited, to say the least) the limit was finally established twelve miles off shore, and still on the line of cape to cape. I believe this prohibition is not as grave a blow to the British industry as our owners and one or two wiseacres among the skippers continue to complain, for no one could maintain that average fish landings on the Hull market have been drastically reduced. While there has been a small drop in catches in comparison with some of the big trips of the past, the point which ought to be stressed and remembered is this: the British industry, unlike its foreign rivals who are more alert to the future, has not paid enough attention to science and technics. Inshore fishing will not be so vital to the profit of a trip when more is known of the nature of cod and haddock, of their feeding habits, of the effect on them of water temperature and current and so on. Nor when ships are fitted out with better methods of stowage and processing of the catch, and when (though the advantage of this is problematical) they are equipped to fish deeper and to stay at sea longer.

But at the time I am speaking of, the loss to skippers, especially the older ones, of grounds they had fished for years (grounds so familiar that some of them had even taken their names from famous skippers) the loss of these tens of thousands of square sea miles of well-known water was a severe blow. Trips going badly with fish coming aboard too slowly could often be put right with two or three days' work on a favourite tow. And so, from time to time, to revive his fortune a skipper would take a chance with the law. Penalties were heavy; a ship arrested by a fisheries protection gunboat and escorted into a port on the violated coast would have her gear confiscated, including her costly trawl warp, her catch expropriated and would remain under arrest until her owners paid a very heavy fine. In all, the cost to an owner of a skipper's outlawry could be in the region of twelve thousand pounds. And yet skippers in need of fish were still prepared to take these risks, so great were the pressures which owners made them work under, so imperative was the demand for success. It is worth noting that the trawler owners' federation do not publish orders prohibiting skippers to break the international laws of fishing limits, nor do they suspend a skipper from command when he is caught red-handed in contravention.

And think of the effect of a night's poaching on us, the crews.

'Get it aboard, Bill,' I once heard a skipper say to his mate. 'I'm going in a bit.' We hung the doors from the galluses, put the trawl inboard, and then he switched out the lights. The weather was freshening and was blowing onshore fairly strongly by the time he reached his marks. I for one hoped that he had made no mistake with them, for close on shore as we were, with no lee and no lights for our work, our reserve of safety had been cut too fine.

That was my first time as a poacher and I was nervous. I thought, after we had got the trawl down and felt our way in the darkness through the tricky manoeuvre, that he was making too severe a demand on both our skill and his own. The cook comforted us with his sympathy as we stood with our tea about the coal black galley and mess room.

'The bastard wants to get arrested. What happens if we put a turn of warp round the screw? What happens if the bastard hurts somebody? Is it him up there who's going to pay his pension?'

We put in two nights' work on that pitch, running off each day before dawn to get in a few hours legal fishing offshore, and we completed our trip from it. But all of us knew, the skipper as well as the crew, that the catching of those three hundred odd kit of fish had taken us too far from a seamanlike regard for the safety of our ship and her company.

For ships are too easily lost. Every year from our three main fishing ports, Hull, Grimsby and Fleetwood, five or more ships go, often with all hands, nearly always with heavy loss of life. I was at sea on the night when two famous ships from Hull went together, steaming into a hurricane off the north side of Iceland. They took all hands with them, forty-two men. I knew nearly all the men in one of the ships, for a few months prior to that dreadful night I had floated in her for four trips.

They called the skipper 'Stormy Steve'. He was a robust, hard-seeming man of fifty or so. I remember he had a pleasant and happy-looking wife who always came down to the dock on sailing morning to say goodbye to him. We used to call her 'Blondie'. Steve was well liked by the crews because not only was he a first-class skipper, always good for a decent living, but also he never bothered to intimidate us with the sack. Ben said to me when he heard I was going with him, 'You'll retire with Steve if you can stand the weather that follows him about. The only reason men leave that old bastard is they get swilled off the log book.'

I am not a superstitious man—in passing I do not recall trawler-men as superstitious in spite of what is said about seafarers—but I never met, with any other man, the sort of weather that dogged old Steve. But there must be a reason for everything, and the fact was that Steve was no more the butt of the weather than any other skipper. They all put up with their share, even the most cautious. No, what made us think the very depression was always standing over Steve was that so many times, when other men had got their gear aboard and were either making a run for the lee or were dodging up comfortably, we would still have it down. He would always try for that last haul. He used to shoot away in appalling weather and though nine times out of ten he managed to run off his gear and spread it correctly, using to the maximum his own skill on the bridge and ours on deck, yet sometimes he would get us into trouble.

I remember once we shot the gear into the eye of weather that was too much for us. She could not keep enough way to run the warps smoothly off the winch drums; moreover the soundings he wanted, and the position of other ships around us, forced him to shoot by the lee (meaning that the weather, as we drove on our line, was on the bow opposite to the side we were fishing her from, pushing us across our own warps). Now to shoot by the lee is a delicate enough manoeuvre in the best of conditions, for the wind swings the hull into the warps as they run, making it impossible to keep a constant tension. The doors of the trawl may fall flat and can then easily sheer off their appointed course and foul one another.

On that day the mate and the man with him, paying warp away at the winch, could not keep steady weight and tension on the wires as they ran off the drums, for the ship, at full speed while we shot, was putting her whaleback right into the waves. Sometimes a big sea would bring her to a standstill and she would falter before picking up her way again. The seas breaking over the whaleback were thrown aft along the wind, cutting our visibility as we sheltered in the doorway and drenching the two men behind the winch. The warps fell slack at every few fathoms, struck the deck hard in front of the winch and then pulled taut again.

Somehow, in spite of the rise and fall, we got them into the towing block without hurting anyone. Steve rang down for towing speed and we could get on deck without much risk of being tumbled about by a sea coming inboard. The mate strolled aft to look at the lay of the warps in the block, then he came forward to us sliding about in the pounds as we got down to the gutting.

'You did that one for practice, lads.' He faced up to the bridge and Steve lowered his lee-side window.

'You've got a turn in your warps,' yelled the mate over the wind.

A man called from the deck, 'Haven't you had enough, you stormy old man?'

That comment would have earned him four weeks on the dock from any other skipper, but Steve never bothered himself about the views of deckies. We used to think he was too busy looking for the next breeze to worry about what went on down among us.

We cleared that gear. It took us, staggering in the weather the way we were, nearly two hours to part those doors locked together, and then we brought it aboard and lashed it and lay up to the wind. But I, like almost all the men who floated with him, became very fond of old Steve; I would not have left him if I had not got hurt.

One night, in another ship, a winter gale off the north of Iceland sent us packing off our ground and we made a run for the lee of a fiord. We were inside and all was quiet; we were sitting in the mess room with a pot of tea waiting to go forward for a sleep. The operator came into the room.

'What, are you resting, sparker?' a man asked.

'No, they've cleared the air. There's two ships north in trouble. They've got a gale and frost.'

I, who many times have nearly cried through the misery of frost, cannot think of a worse way to die than the death which came to those men after the events of that night. They do not often come together for the wind usually has plenty of west or east in it and when it blows strong blows away the frost. But when it comes in hard from the north, bearing its own frost with it, then it will kill. Then the sea piles aboard; it runs away through the scuppers but the wet film that remains freezes, and it happens again and again, for in that air there is nothing to stop it, until the ship's steel is covered by a lens of ice. As it thickens you can break off chips. While this is happening the scud that blows off the sea right over her and the white water from the waves she has broken into freezes too, and she begins to labour as the frozen weight bears down. She will be hard to steer because she was not designed to carry weight where she is massing it now. She begins to lose her outline as the frost piles up over capstan, winch, upperworks, as her rigging becomes sheeted in black ice. All she needs to clear herself is a few hours of warmth. But there is no warmth. The poor men try to work the ice off her.

We heard from Steve and the other skipper through the radio; in that terrible weather the crews got at the ice with axes, and where they could find an unfrozen outlet they piped hot water from the engine-room out of it. But the ships replaced ice faster than the men could break it off. By now they were in the worst of the gale, the weather became so wild that it seemed to me extravagant, vindictive, for quite a modest breeze by then would have finished them. No one could help them though we could all hear them. The fleet was stopped from going to their aid by the very conditions which had put the two ships in distress. Steven told all of us, listening hopelessly, that she had taken a list. He set his men to the boats but the useless, fool things were iced hard into the davits. I say now, God rot the owners who would not spend enough money to put rubber rafts aboard; with them they might have saved themselves, but in that weather the boats, even if the crew could have chopped them clear of the davits, would have smashed against the ship's side in launching. Soon after, they heard old Steve say, 'She's going', and then the other one went and forty-two were lost. When those men came to their last few hours they were already too close to fatigue; they must have passed them before they died beyond its edge and nearly frozen.

There should be a change in the conditions under which the crews of British trawlers have to earn their living. The fishermen of other nations, who only know the way we work and nothing of our history, do not understand. Professionally they look upon us with a sort of sympathetic condescension mixed with admiration. Years ago I was in a ship blown out of the eastern end of the White Sea and we had to run for shelter into Murmansk. The port authorities there did not bother to be suspicious of us; it must have been only too clear that we were what we looked like, namely fishermen sheltering, and they left us the freedom of the port.

There were a number of trawlers of about the same class as our own lying in there, German ships which the Russians had confiscated and were working while they constructed their own fleet. A hand on the deck of one of them signed to me to climb aboard. The differences in design on deck and in her accommodation were small and without thinking I followed him aft to the mess room. There we began to drink schnapps and vodka. Others in the crew joined us and I returned to our ship for what was left in my bottle and for two of my shipmates. We mustered more than a bottle and a half of rum and rejoined the Russians. In a welter of liquor, and with signs between them and us we made friends and they tried to tell us of the way they fished their ships. When they found out from us, in their turn, how we had to work, one of them, in a most affable way, made at us the universal gesture of an imbecile, a roll of the eyes and forefinger to pate.

That Russian sailor was only partly right, for with no tradition of unity behind us, with the industry overmanned, with time ashore so limited, with the very nature of the job preventing the gathering of a majority of men, what chance did we have of standing up to the owners? How easy it has been for them to keep the crews, and the individuals in the crews, apart from one another.

Even so we won rights for ourselves. There was a time, and it was not long before I came into the industry, when trawlermen had no right to a watch below but worked the fish until they could work no more. They tumbled on their beds for four or five hours only when the skipper, who had put the same strains on himself, admitted that the fatigue of the crew had long endangered the safety of the ship. Then from that unconsciousness that does not deserve the name of rest, still fully dressed, some of them even in sea boots and frocks, still hopelessly tired, they came on deck and worked again until they were finished men. And so throughout the trip until, when the fish room was filled, they took her home.

That could no longer be done to us, neither could the owners turn the ships round in twenty-four hours and send the men back to sea.

There have been strikes in the industry: I was myself in one where for weeks we refused to sign. We were out to gain more rest by increasing ships' companies, and more money for ourselves from the huge fortunes made in the ownership of the trawlers and the organisation of the market. We failed and we went back to conditions as I have described them throughout this book. Now old shipmates tell me that changes are about to be forced on the Fish Dock, for young men are proving hard to tempt into the industry, and the struggle to organise is being won.

Hull, which for years was the port which landed most deepwater fish in the world, holds its place no longer. But I say that it is British trawler owners, and especially those from Hull, who have lost us the highest place, for they have always charged the men who caught their fish too high a price in vitality and even in life.

I have been ashore now for three years and the writing of this book has wrung out what sea water there was left in me. I believe I could never be a trawlerman again, though when people ask me how I earn my living I tell them still that once I was that. They say that a man is what he does: well, I did that. I know that whatever sort of man I am now was mainly put together on the deck of a trawler. Not much more can happen to me except the extension of this or that power, the retraction of another. I learnt things you need to be very careful with, good and evil things about myself, things which cause a man to waste time by lavishing love and hate on himself. Most of us had to be syco-phants ('shit-eating' we called it) because that was one of the tacit terms of signing on, but I am adult enough now to hate, not myself for eating it, but the economics which forced that daily diet down us. Most of us had to learn the rudiments of unselfishness and to dredge up courage from somewhere because without them a man could barely contemplate a second trip. Things will change for the better, for trawlermen; science joined with their own in-creasing skill must bring them at least the rewards in relief of toil, rest ashore and security, which for years they have earned but have not been paid. I believe that a struggle lies ahead of them and I believe they will win it. As far as an ex-trawlerman can be, I am with them. I am glad I went.

*Line Drawings*

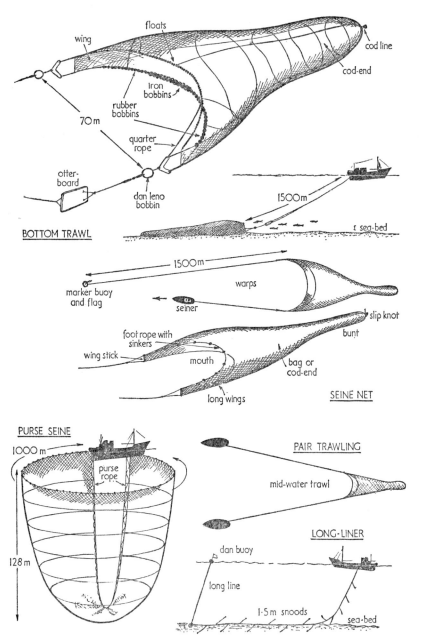

floats

wing

cod line

cod-end

Iron bobbins

rubber bobbins

70 m

quarter rope

otter-board

dan leno bobbin

BOTTOM TRAWL

1500m

sea-bed

1500m

marker buoy and flag

warps

seiner

slip knot

bunt

foot rope with sinkers

wing stick

mouth

bag or cod-end

long wings

SEINE NET

PURSE SEINE

1000 m

purse rope

PAIR TRAWLING

mid-water trawl

128 m

LONG-LINER

dan buoy

long line

1·5 m snoods

sea-bed

Methods of trawling and drifting

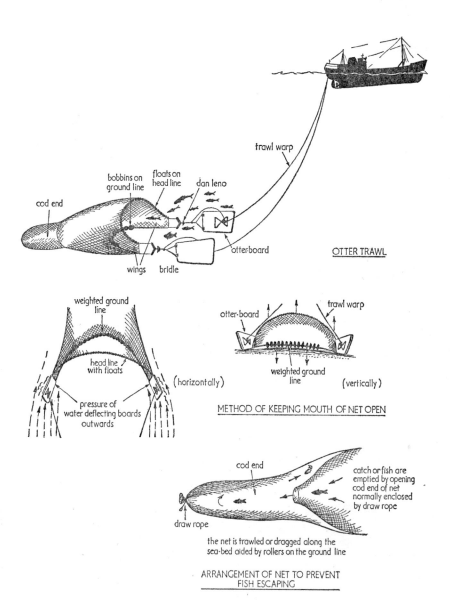

trawl warp

bobbins on
ground line

floats on
head line

dan leno

cod end

wings    bridle

otterboard

OTTER TRAWL

weighted ground
line

head line
with floats

(horizontally)

pressure of
water deflecting boards
outwards

otter-board

trawl warp

weighted ground
line

(vertically)

METHOD OF KEEPING MOUTH OF NET OPEN

cod end

catch or fish are
emptied by opening
cod end of net
normally enclosed
by draw rope

draw rope

the net is trawled or dragged along the
sea-bed aided by rollers on the ground line

ARRANGEMENT OF NET TO PREVENT
FISH ESCAPING

Methods of trawling and drifting

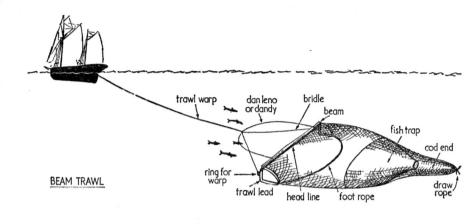

trawl warp    dan leno    bridle
              or dandy         beam

                                        fish trap

                                              cod end

ring for
warp                                          draw
                                              rope
BEAM TRAWL    trawl lead   head line   foot rope

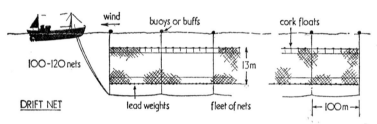

wind →        buoys or buffs        cork floats

100-120 nets                                      13m

DRIFT NET     lead weights    fleet of nets    |← 100m →|

## Methods of trawling and drifting

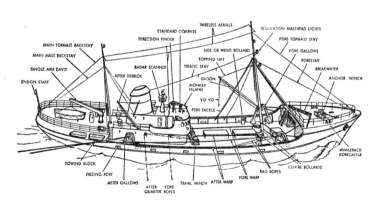

WIRELESS AERIALS
STANDARD COMPASS              REGULATION MASTHEAD LIGHTS
DIRECTION FINDER                    FORE TOPMAST STAY
MAIN TOPMAST BACKSTAY                          FORE GALLOWS
MAIN MAST BACKSTAY          SIDE OR WING BOLLARD
                           TOPPING LIFT          FORESTAY
SINGLE ARM DAVIT    RADAR SCANNER   TRIATIC STAY      BREAKWATER
                    AFTER DERRICK        GILSON      ANCHOR WINCH
ENSIGN STAFF                         MONKEY
                                     ISLAND
                                     YO YO
                                     FISH TACKLE
                                                      WHALEBACK
                                                      FORECASTLE
TOWING BLOCK                                    CENTRE BOLLARDS
     FREEING PORT                          BAG ROPES
       AFTER GALLOWS    AFTER  FORE           FORE WARP
                        QUARTER ROPES
                              TRAWL WINCH  AFTER WARP

## Deck layout of a deep-sea side trawler